BATTLE EXTRAVAGONZO

Written by **PAUL TOBIN**

Art by **TIM LATTIE**

Colors by **MATT J. RAINWATER**

Letters by **STEVE DUTRO**

Cover by **RON CHAN**

Plants vs. Zombies: Battle Extravagonzo

DARK HORSE BOOKS

President and Publisher **MIKE RICHARDSON**
Editor **PHILIP R. SIMON**
Assistant Editor **MEGAN WALKER**
Designer **BRENNAN THOME**
Digital Art Technician **CHRISTINA McKENZIE**

Special thanks to Leigh Beach, A.J. Rathbun, Kristen Star, Jeremy Vanhoozer, and everyone at PopCap Games.

Scholastic edition: August 2017
ISBN 978-1-50670-547-7

10 9 8 7 6 5 4 3 2 1
Printed in China

DarkHorse.com
PopCap.com

No plants were harmed in the making of this graphic novel. However, in their ring battles, numerous zombies and cohorts like Chestbeard and Mr. Stubbins absolutely were. Multiple times.

PLANTS vs. ZOMBIES: BATTLE EXTRAVAGONZO | Published by Dark Horse Books, a division of Dark Horse Comics, Inc., 10956 SE Main Street, Milwaukie, OR 97222 | International Licensing: (503) 905-2377 | To find a comics shop in your area, call the Comic Shop Locator Service toll-free at 1-888-266-4226. |

Library of Congress Cataloging-in-Publication Data

Names: Tobin, Paul, 1965-, author. | Lattie, Tim, artist. | Rainwater, Matthew J., colourist. | Dutro, Steve, letterer.
Title: Plants vs. zombies. Battle extravagonzo / written by Paul Tobin ; art by Tim Lattie ; colors by Matt J. Rainwater ; letters by Steve Dutro ; cover by Ron Chan.
Other titles: Plants versus zombies. Battle extravagonzo | Battle extravagonzo
Description: First edition. | Milwaukie, OR : Dark Horse Books, 2017. | Series: Plants vs. zombies ; 7 | Summary: Evil mastermind Zomboss wants to build a zombie factory and position his new army in the best location possible, but Crazy Dave, his helpers Nate and Patrice, and their batch of intelligent plants, will try to get the factory for themselves.
Identifiers: LCCN 2016057713 | ISBN 9781506701899 (hardback)
Subjects: LCSH: Graphic novels. | CYAC: Graphic novels. | Zombies--Fiction. | Science fiction. | BISAC: JUVENILE FICTION / Comics & Graphic Novels / Media Tie-In. | JUVENILE FICTION / Comics & Graphic Novels / General. | JUVENILE FICTION / Action & Adventure / General.
Classification: LCC PZ7.7.T62 Ph 2017 | DDC 741.5/973--dc23
LC record available at https://lccn.loc.gov/2016057713

I MADE YOU TWO PIES!
I MADE YOU A PIE TOO!
I WILL EAT A PIE!
I WILL EAT TWO PIES!
A PLEASANT DAY IN NEIGHBORVILLE, HOME TO THE FRIENDLIEST NEIGHBORS IN THE WORLD!
HOME TO CRAZY DAVE!
FLOOOP!
NEW INVENTION
Baseball TOAST
Very IMPORTANT
HOME TO SOME CONFUSED PEOPLE WATCHING CRAZY DAVE!
WHP
PLAFF!
QUACK?
HOME TO THIS DUCK, WHICH IS NOT REALLY A PART OF OUR STORY.
HA! ≥URPP!≤ I... ≥URRP!≤... I WIN!
OKAY. I ADMIT IT. I BET YOU THAT YOU COULDN'T EAT THIRTY PANCAKES, BUT... AMAZINGLY, HORRIBLY... YOU DID IT.
HOME TO NATE TIMELY AND PATRICE BLAZING!

HA! URPP! THAT MEANS...
...I GET YOUR PANCAKES.

EIGHBORVILLE! HOME TO ALL THESE POOR, UNFORTUNATE, AND INNOCENT PEOPLE WHO ARE ABOUT TO GET CAUGHT UP IN A CATACLYSMIC CONFLICT OF UNIMAGINABLE DEVASTATION.
UM, WHAT?

NEIGHBORVILLE! HOME TO THIS VAN.
NOT FULL of ZOMBIES
NO WORRIES

AND THIS ONE!
GARDEN SUPPLIES
PLUS ICE CREAM
AND DISCO
"HAVE A NICE DAY!"

AND THIS DOG!
SNIFF!
SNIFF!
Z-BOSS
SNIFF!

NEIGHBORVILLE! HOME TO...
HRRK!!
Z-BOSS

...ZOMBIES!

AND MORE ZOMBIES!
ZOMBIE APPRECIATION SOCIETY
#1
RAH! RAH! RAH!

AND PLANTS!
BURST!

AND MORE PLANTS!
PLANT APPRECIATION SOCIETY
#1
PLANT APPRECIATION SOCIETY (BEE DIVISION)
OOOOO... FROM NOW ON, NO MORE THAN FORTY PANCAKES.

OKAY, EVERYONE-- IT'S TIME!

SQUEAK
SQUEAK
TONIGHT TONIGHT TONIGHT
PLANTS vs ZOMBIES
BATTLE EXTRAVA-GONZO
It's All Settled in THE RING!
WHO will KNOW VICTORY?
WHO WILL KNOW THE AGONY of Defeat?
(ALSO TONIGHT: MRS. PLIMPDALE'S 1st GRADE COLORING CONTEST! WHO WILL STAY WITHIN THE LINES?)
WE'RE READY!
LET'S FIGHT!
SQUICK!

EARLIER...
WRATHBUNS BREAD FACTORY
HOME OF
Sweaty Beet Bread
THERE'S NO HOPE! ALL IS LOST!

WE'RE GOING OUT OF BUSINESS!
BILL

Sweaty Beet Bread
Eat this Bread! TURN this Red!
APPARENTLY, NOBODY WANTS TO BUY BREAD WITH A SPECIAL INGREDIENT THAT MAKES YOU TURN BEET RED, LIKE ME!
I'M GOING TO HAVE TO SELL THE FACTORY!

TWEET TWEET!

CHIRP CHIRP CHIRP!

QUACK!
CHIRP!

THIS IS THE CHANCE I'VE BEEN WAITING FOR, MR. STUBBINS!
SQUICK!

HERE...RIGHT IN THE HEART OF THE CITY, FROM WHERE I COULD STRIKE OUT AT MY ENEMIES... I WILL CREATE A ZOMBIE FACTORY!!
"A FACTORY THAT WILL PRODUCE AN UNENDING STREAM OF ZOMBIES! ZOMBIES OF ALL KINDS!
"BUCKETHEAD ZOMBIES! GARGANTUARS! MINDLESS ZOMBIES! EXTRA-MINDLESS ZOMBIES! POWERFUL ZOMBIES! LOYAL ZOMBIES!"
CHONNGA!
IMP-IN-AN-INSTANT
CHONNGA!
ZOMBIE-O-MATIC
POP SMARTS
CHONNGA!
CHONNGA!
BAM BAM BAM BAM
HMM... I SUPPOSE IF I'M GOING TO INCREASE MY ARMY, I'LL ALSO NEED MORE SHOES, CLOTHES, BUCKETS...
...BALLOONS, STILTS, BAGPIPES, SNACK MACHINES, HAIR CONDITIONER, HARMONICAS, SNORKELS, GUMBALLS, NAME TAGS...
...AND A FEW THOUSAND MORE OF MY GLOSSY AUTOGRAPHED PHOTOS TO HAND OUT.
THE IMPORTANT THING IS-- I SENSE AN OPPORTUNITY.
AND WHEN OPPORTUNITY STRIKES...
MUNCH MUNCH MUNCH
RASPBRAINBERRY POP SMART
MUNCH MUNCH MUNCH

WRATHBUNS BREAD FACTORY
(IMPORTANT PERSON ENTRANCE)
KNOCK!
KNOCK!
...ZOMBOSS STRIKES!
KNOCK!

OW! MY KNUCKLES!
I STRUCK TOO HARD.

HELLO? CAN I HELP YOU?
OH, I THINK I'M THE ONE WHO CAN HELP YOU.
I'M PREPARED TO MAKE A VERY GENEROUS OFFER TO PURCHASE YOUR FACTORY.
DISGUISE!

BEET IT
OH! UH...REALLY? THAT'S GREAT! WHAT CAN YOU OFFER ME?
I'M PREPARED TO GIVE YOU THE ASTOUNDING OFFER OF...TWELVE DOLLARS AND FOURTEEN CENTS...PLUS A LIFETIME SUPPLY OF...

REVEAL!
...NOT BEING THREATENED BY ZOMBOSS!
HAHAHA!

HA HA HA! HAAA! HA!
QUACK QUACK!
CHIRP CHIRP!

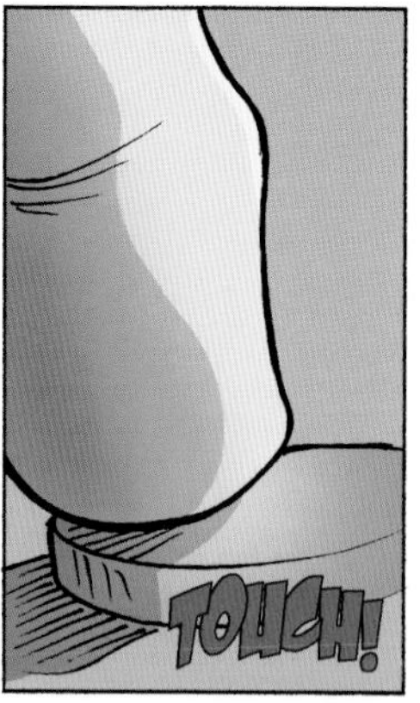

WHAT'S HAPPENING?

MY UNCLE DAVE'S PUTTING THE FINISHING TOUCHES ON HIS BIG, SHINY ICE-CREAM-MAKING MACHINE.

CRANNK CRANNK

TOUCH!

KLANK!

IT'S A MACHINE THAT MAKES SMALLER MACHINES THAT CAN MAKE AN INCREDIBLE ARRAY OF ICE CREAM FLAVORS!

OGRIBBLE BLARN QUIQSTEIN DUCK DUCK GOOSE QUAGHOLLOW!
UNCLE DAVE SAYS THAT HE WANTS TO MAKE *HUNDREDS* OF HIS BIG, SHINY ICE-CREAM-MAKING MACHINES.
KLANK!
CRANNK CRANNK
CRANNK
?!
CROAAAK
"THEN HE COULD EITHER PROVIDE ENOUGH ICE-CREAM MACHINES FOR EVERYONE IN NEIGHBORVILLE...
"...OR MAKE AN ICE-CREAM MOUNTAIN AND SKI JUMP INTO AN ICE-CREAM POOL."
AND...THERE'S ONLY *ONE* PLACE IN *ALL* OF NEIGHBORVILLE SUITABLE FOR UNCLE DAVE'S ICE-CREAM-MACHINE FACTORY.
LUCKILY, THE PLACE JUST WENT UP FOR SALE. I'M TALKING ABOUT...
"...THE WRATHBUNS BREAD FACTORY."

Foreboding MUSIC
FORESHADOW CONFLICTS
INSTILL MENACE
TOO MUCH CHEESE?
DUNN DUNN DUNNNN

AND SO...
MY CLIENT, MR. TOP HAT WITH MUSTACHE, HAS BEEN CONSIDERING YOUR RESPECTIVE OFFERS.
YOU, MR. Z. BOSS, HAVE MADE AN OFFER OF... TWELVE DOLLARS AND FOURTEEN CENTS, AND ALSO A PROMISE OF NO BRAIN EATING.
WHILE, YOU, MR. CRAZY DAVE...
...YOU'VE MADE AN OFFER OF...LET'S SEE...

...A PAPIER-MÂCHÉ SCULPTURE OF YOURSELF, A MAILBOX SAND-WICH...
...AND AN AUTOGRAPHED PICTURE OF A PEPPERONI PIZZA.
BEST WISHES TO MY BIGGEST FAN
a PIZZA
USA

GENTLEMEN, I'M AFRAID THESE OFFERS ARE...NOT SUFFICIENT.
USA

HERE IS WHAT MY CLIENT WOULD LIKE.
THAT MUCH ?!?!

OH, I WASN'T DONE YET.

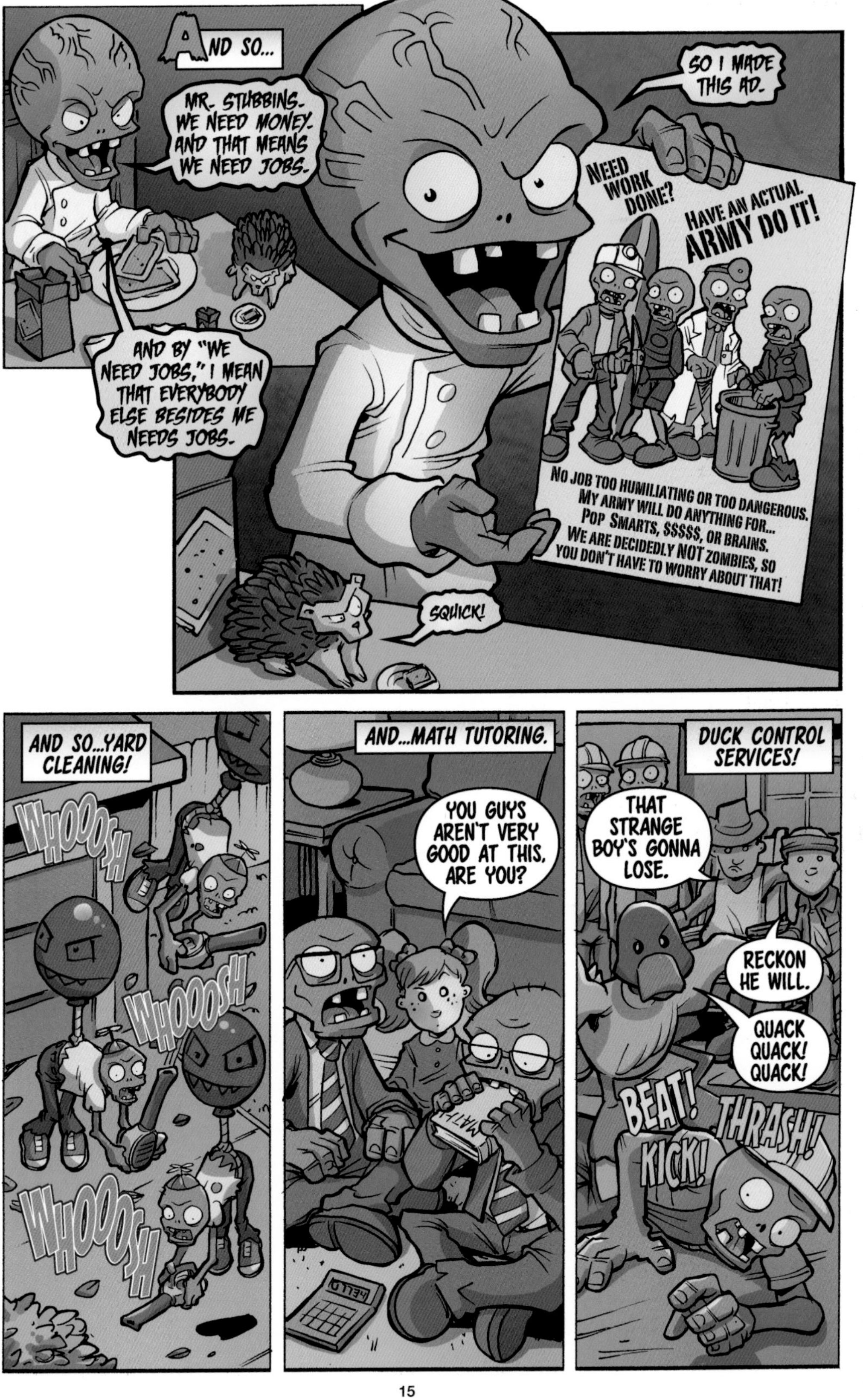

AND SO...
MR. STUBBINS. WE NEED MONEY. AND THAT MEANS WE NEED JOBS.
AND BY "WE NEED JOBS," I MEAN THAT EVERYBODY ELSE BESIDES ME NEEDS JOBS.
SO I MADE THIS AD.
NEED WORK DONE?
HAVE AN ACTUAL ARMY DO IT!
NO JOB TOO HUMILIATING OR TOO DANGEROUS. MY ARMY WILL DO ANYTHING FOR... POP SMARTS, $$$$$, OR BRAINS. WE ARE DECIDEDLY NOT ZOMBIES, SO YOU DON'T HAVE TO WORRY ABOUT THAT!
SQUICK!

YOU'RE TERRIBLE AT THIS!
CHAUFFEUR!

CRASH TEST DUMMY!
YOU'RE PERFECT AT THIS!

HAIR STYLIST!
BRAINS.
BRAINZZZZ.
WELL, THEY'RE CERTAINLY VERY ATTENTIVE.

HMM...THE CAKE FROSTING WAS SUPPOSED TO SAY "CONGRATULATIONS ON GRADUATING WITH HONORS, TIMMY!" BUT...
CAKE DECORATING!

...ALL IT SAYS IS "BRAINS BRAINS BRAINS."
BRAINSSS?
BRAINZZ
BRAINZZZ
BRAINZ

HONESTLY, I'VE NEVER BEEN HAPPIER WITH A SECRETARY.
OFFICE WORK!
SQUICK.

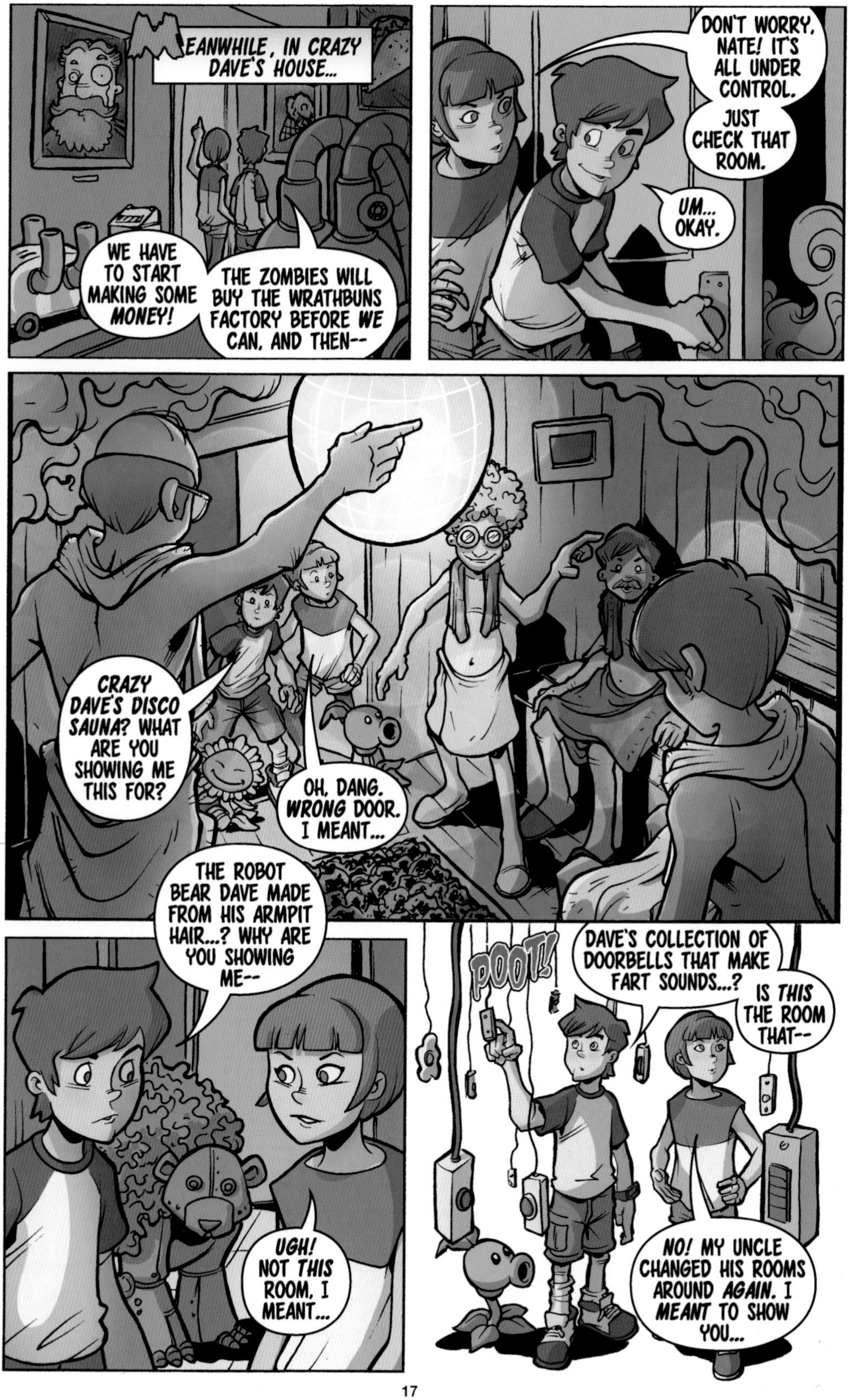

CRAZY DAVE'S DISCO SAUNA? WHAT ARE YOU SHOWING ME THIS FOR?

OH, DANG. WRONG DOOR. I MEANT...

THE ROBOT BEAR DAVE MADE FROM HIS ARMPIT HAIR...? WHY ARE YOU SHOWING ME--

UGH! NOT THIS ROOM, I MEANT...

POOT!

DAVE'S COLLECTION OF DOORBELLS THAT MAKE FART SOUNDS...?

IS THIS THE ROOM THAT--

NO! MY UNCLE CHANGED HIS ROOMS AROUND AGAIN. I MEANT TO SHOW YOU...

WHOA.
...THIS!

IS THIS ALL *REAL*?
YEAH. I'VE BEEN MEANING TO TELL YOU THAT MY UNCLE IS *INCREDIBLY* RICH, OWING TO HIS...
EXTRA DISCO CHAMPIONSHIP TROPHIES

"...LIFETIME OF PRIZES FROM DISCO COMPETITIONS.
BIG DOOZY DISCO DANCE MARATHON:
HOUR NUMBER
57

"AND THEN, OF COURSE, HE GOT HIS MIRROR-BALL ENDORSEMENTS."
CRAZY DAVE'S MIRROR BALLS WILL LITERALLY DRIVE YOU INSANE!
(NO, SERIOUSLY, YOU WILL ENTIRELY LOSE YOUR MIND AND ANY SENSE OF REASON)

NOW ALL WE HAVE TO DO IS PUT ENOUGH MONEY IN THIS WHEELBARROW AND...

...AVOID THE ANGRY STARES FROM THE *ROBOT PIGGY BANKS*, AND...

SMACK!
QUACK!
THRASH
SUPLEX!
...TAKE THIS MONEY TO MR. TOP HAT WITH MUSTACHE.

ROLL
ROLL
ROLL
ROLL

HMM? PATRICE...?

I SEE THEM. GET READY TO--

--ROLL!
ROLL
ROLL
ROLL
ROLL

SHAMBLE
SHAMBLE
SHAMBLE
SHAMBLE

FASTER!
FASTER!!!
ROLL
ROLL
ROLL
ROLL

WHIP
WHIP
WHIP
SQUIIICK!

DUCK à L'ORANGE
ROLL
ROLL
ROLL
ROLL

SQUICK!
SQUICK!
SQUICK!
DUCK à LO

ROLL
RUN
RUN
ROLL
SHAMBLE
SHAMBLE

IT'S A TIE!

HMM...I SEE THAT YOU'VE BOTH BROUGHT THE NECESSARY FUNDS, AND THAT YOU'VE TIED ON YOUR ARRIVAL.

SO BE IT! THERE IS ONLY *ONE* WAY TO TRULY SETTLE THIS, THEN. MY CLIENT, MR. TOP HAT WITH MUSTACHE, WILL BE...

...JUDGING YOU IN AN *ALL-OUT BATTLE* IN THE MOST *DANGEROUS* PLACE POSSIBLE!

AN ARENA OF *INCREDIBLE DANGER!*

WHERE THE *SLIGHTEST MISCALCULATION* CAN LEAD TO YOUR *DOOM!*

A PLACE WHERE YOU WILL STARE INTO EACH OTHER'S EYES, *SNARLING, GRITTING* YOUR TEETH...

...BRINGING ALL YOUR *BATTLE PROWESS* TO THE FOREFRONT, *SKIRTING* THE *RAZOR'S EDGE* LEST YOU BE CAST INTO THE *DARKEST ABYSS!*

I'M TALKING ABOUT THE *DEADLIEST* ARENA IN ALL THE KNOWN LANDS...

SO *LINE UP!* DON YOUR *BATTLE GEAR*, LET CRY THE *DOGS OF WAR*, FOR WE MEET IN *COMBAT* AT...

...THE NEGOTIATING TABLE!

OH. I THOUGHT WE WERE GOING TO FIGHT.
YEAH. ME TOO. NICE SPEECH, THOUGH.

SOON...
OKAY, IF WE'RE GOING TO BE DEALING WITH LAWYERS AND JUDGES, EVERYBODY HAS TO LOOK THEIR VERY BEST.

MEANWHILE...
IT'S...PROBABLY BEST YOU JUST CARRY THESE IN FRONT OF YOU.

AND...
STAY STILL! STAY STILL!!
CRAZY DAVE'S SUPER-GROOMER

AND SO...
...PURSUANT TO CLAUSE FIFTEEN OF PARAGRAPH SEVEN...
AND...FIFTEEN MINUTES LATER...
...ROYALTIES OF 6.7 PERCENT TRIGGERED ON A SEMIANNUAL BASIS...
AND...FORTY MINUTES LATER...
...NOTWITHSTANDING ELIMINATION OF FLUX CAPACITORS...
AND...AN HOUR LATER...
...REFER, IF YOU WILL, TO PARAGRAPH SEVEN, PASSAGE THREE, REGARDING THE ANNUITY FLOW CHARTS.
AND...SIX HOURS LATER...
FURTHERMORE, IN ACCORDANCE WITH HOW AN ORIGINATING SUMMONS FALLS UNDER JURISDICTION OF AN ORDER IN COUNCIL, THE TWO PARTIES SHALL--

THIS PARTY IS OVER!

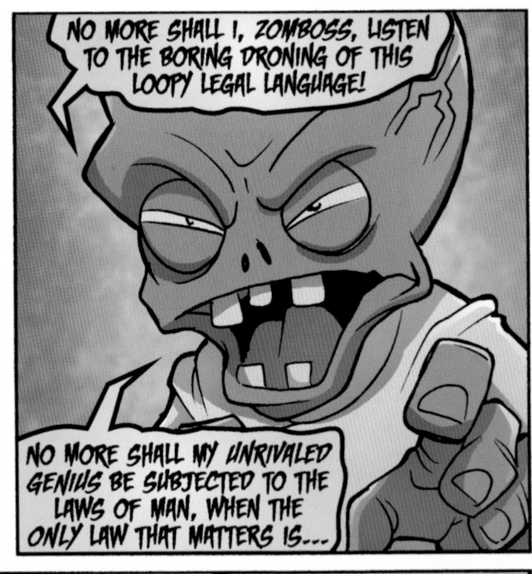
NO MORE SHALL I, ZOMBOSS, LISTEN TO THE BORING DRONING OF THIS LOOPY LEGAL LANGUAGE!
NO MORE SHALL MY UNRIVALED GENIUS BE SUBJECTED TO THE LAWS OF MAN, WHEN THE ONLY LAW THAT MATTERS IS...

...THE LAW OF CONQUEST!
WHMMP

YOU! I CHALLENGE YOU FOR THE RIGHTS TO THE WRATHBUNS BREAD FACTORY!

CLIKK
I CHALLENGE YOU IN THE STREETS! I CHALLENGE YOU ON THE ROOFTOPS!
I CHALLENGE YOU IN THE DAYTIME! I CHALLENGE YOU AT NIGHT!

EXCEPT FOR BETWEEN 7:00 AND 8:00 PM, BECAUSE I DON'T WANT TO MISS MY FAVORITE TELEVISION SHOW.

SERIOUSLY, THOUGH. I DO CHALLENGE YOU.

WHISPER WHISPER WHISPER
HMM. NO, I DIDN'T SEE THE DUCK. YES, I'LL TELL THEM.

EVERYONE...? MY CLIENT, MR. TOP HAT WITH MUSTACHE, HAS DECIDED THAT THE SALE OF THE WRATHBUNS BREAD FACTORY WILL GO TO...

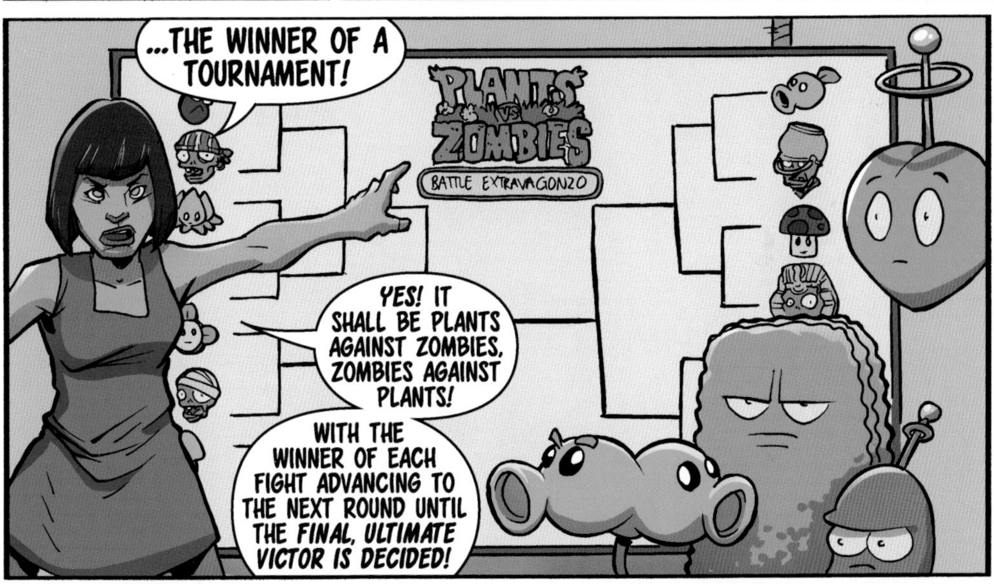
...THE WINNER OF A TOURNAMENT!
PLANTS VS ZOMBIES
BATTLE EXTRAVAGONZO
YES! IT SHALL BE PLANTS AGAINST ZOMBIES, ZOMBIES AGAINST PLANTS!
WITH THE WINNER OF EACH FIGHT ADVANCING TO THE NEXT ROUND UNTIL THE FINAL, ULTIMATE VICTOR IS DECIDED!

THE TOURNAMENT STARTS TOMORROW MORNING!

SO, YOU'D BEST...

...GET READY.

YES! A BATTLE! THIS IS FANTASTIC!

BUMP
PRESS

BUMP

BUMP
BUMP

BUMP

BUMP
BUMP
BUMP

=SIGH= I'LL GET THAT FOR YOU.
PRESS

TOMORROW, WE FIGHT!

AHHH!

THMMP

LATE TOMORROW.

AND SO...
THIS WEEKEND!
HEROIC PLANTS
BATTLE
VILLAINOUS ZOMBIES
WITNESS THE RAW
MIGHT OF MELONS
AND PEASHOOTERS
AGAINST THE
PERPLEXED GARGANTUARS
PLUS FIREWORKS!
RING IN THE WEEKEND
IN THE RING!
MAIL

BRING YOUR KIDS! BRING YOUR MOM! BRING THE WHOLE FAMILY! BRING A PSYCHIATRIST, BECAUSE IT'S GOING TO GET CRAZY, CRAZY, CRAZY!

ZOMBIE
HEROES
MAKE FIGHTING
MUCH
PUNCH!

THWOOSH!
THWOOSH!
VS
VS
VS
OOO! A FIGHT!

AND NOW, FOR SOME COMMENTARY ON THE BIG UPCOMING PLANTS VS. ZOMBIES BATTLE TOURNAMENT, LET'S GO TO FELDSPAR AND CHUGGERS AT BRAIN-Z, THE ZOMBIE SPORTS NETWORK!

ZOMBIE TRANSLATOR
BRAIN-Z
ZOMBIE SPORTS NETWORK

ZOMBIE TRANSLATOR
BRAINS?

BRAIN-Z
ZOMBIE SPORTS NETWORK

BRAINS?
BRAINS?

BRAIN-Z
ZOMBIE SPORTS NETWORK

GNAW
GNAW
CRACKLE
GNAW

ZOMBIE TRANSLATOR
BRAINSSSSS?

REMEMBER, RULES ARE THERE FOR A REASON...TO KEEP EVERYONE SAFE.

SO ALWAYS OBEY THE REFEREE'S COMMANDS, REMEMBER TO FIGHT FAIR, AND BE ON YOUR ABSOLUTE BEST BEHAVIOR.

ELSEWHERE...
ABOVE ALL ELSE, CHEAT WHENEVER YOU CAN.

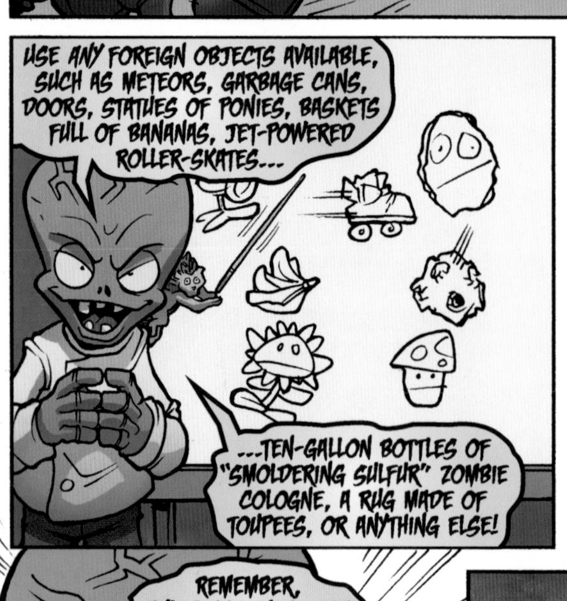
USE ANY FOREIGN OBJECTS AVAILABLE, SUCH AS METEORS, GARBAGE CANS, DOORS, STATUES OF PONIES, BASKETS FULL OF BANANAS, JET-POWERED ROLLER-SKATES...
...TEN-GALLON BOTTLES OF "SMOLDERING SULFUR" ZOMBIE COLOGNE, A RUG MADE OF TOUPEES, OR ANYTHING ELSE!

SQUICK!
TRY TO STEAL THEIR PIZZA!

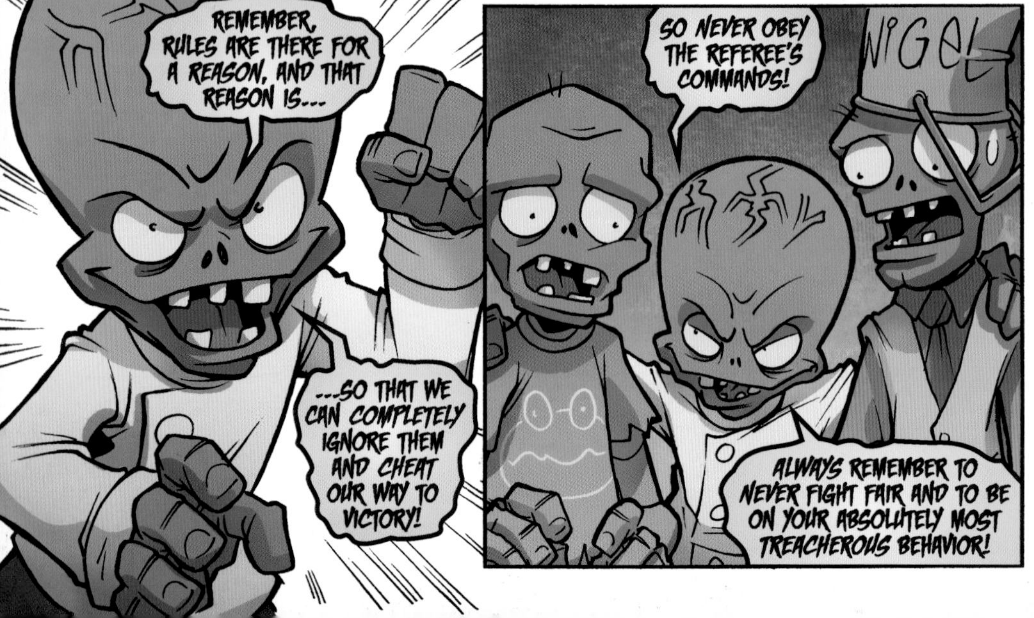
REMEMBER, RULES ARE THERE FOR A REASON, AND THAT REASON IS...
...SO THAT WE CAN COMPLETELY IGNORE THEM AND CHEAT OUR WAY TO VICTORY!
SO NEVER OBEY THE REFEREE'S COMMANDS!
NIGEL
ALWAYS REMEMBER TO NEVER FIGHT FAIR AND TO BE ON YOUR ABSOLUTELY MOST TREACHEROUS BEHAVIOR!

PLANTS VS. ZOMBIES
EXTRAVAGONZO
TONIGHT!
TONIGHT!
TONIGHT!
FRED THE SUNFLOWER VS. IMP
HYPNO-SHROOM VS. CONEHEAD ZOMBIE
BALLOON ZOMBIE VS. GRRAWRRBEAR
CRAZY DAVE VS. DISCO ZOMBIE
CACTUS VS. FOOTBALL-ZOMBIE
CATTAIL VS. MR. STUBBINS
JALAPEÑO VS. CHEST BEARD
ZOMBIE YETI VS. POTATO MINE
JEFF THE BLOOMERANG VS. NEWSPAPER ZOMBIE
NATE VS. BUCKETHEAD ZOMBIE
PATRICE VS. FROGPANTS
TUGBOAT VS. CHERRY-BOMB
SCAREDY-SHROOM VS. ZOMBOSS!
MELON-PULT VS. SCREENDOOR-ZOMBIE
CHOMPER VS. NIGEL-BLIMPBOTTOM
NIGEL
SNOW PEA VS. BUNGEE-ZOMBIE!
SQUASH VS. GAR-GANTUAR

AND SOON...THE FIGHTS BEGIN!
LADIES AND GENTLEMEN...
...AND ALSO PLANTS AND ZOMBIES AND MRS. ISAACSON'S THIRD GRADE CLASS!
PvsZ
WE WELCOME YOU TO THE PLANTS VERSUS ZOMBIES FIGHTING TOURNAMENT...
...WITH THE WINNER WINNING THE RIGHT TO BUY THE WRATHBUNS BREAD FACTORY FROM MR. TOP HAT WITH MUSTACHE!
THE RULES OF THE TOURNAMENT ARE SIMPLE.
FIGHTER 1
FIGHTER 2
TWO CONTESTANTS WILL RUMBLE IN THE RING!
THE WINNER ADVANCES TO THE NEXT ROUND!
FIGHTER 1
NEXT ROUND
FIGHTER 2
THE LOSER... DOES NOT!
NOPE

Round One...Fight!
CACTUS
VS.
FOOTBALL ZOMBIE

WHTT
WHTT
WHTT

THPP
THPP
THPP

HEH HEH!

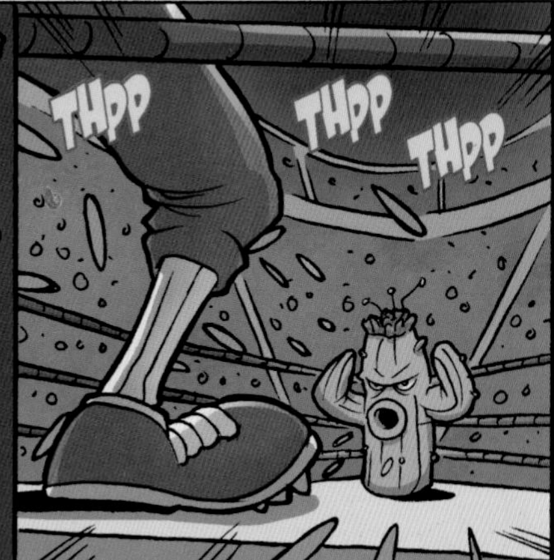
THPP
THPP
THPP

OH, NO!

DOINK!

Cactus loses!

Round One...Fight!
HYPNO-SHROOM
VS.
CONEHEAD ZOMBIE

Hypno-Shroom...wins!
WHAT!? GRKKK! WHY ARE YOU ATTACKING... ME?!

Round One...Rumble!
PEASHOOTER
VS.
DIGGER ZOMBIE

DIG DIG DIG

DIG DIG DIG

P-TOO
P-TOO

GAHH!

Peashooter wins!

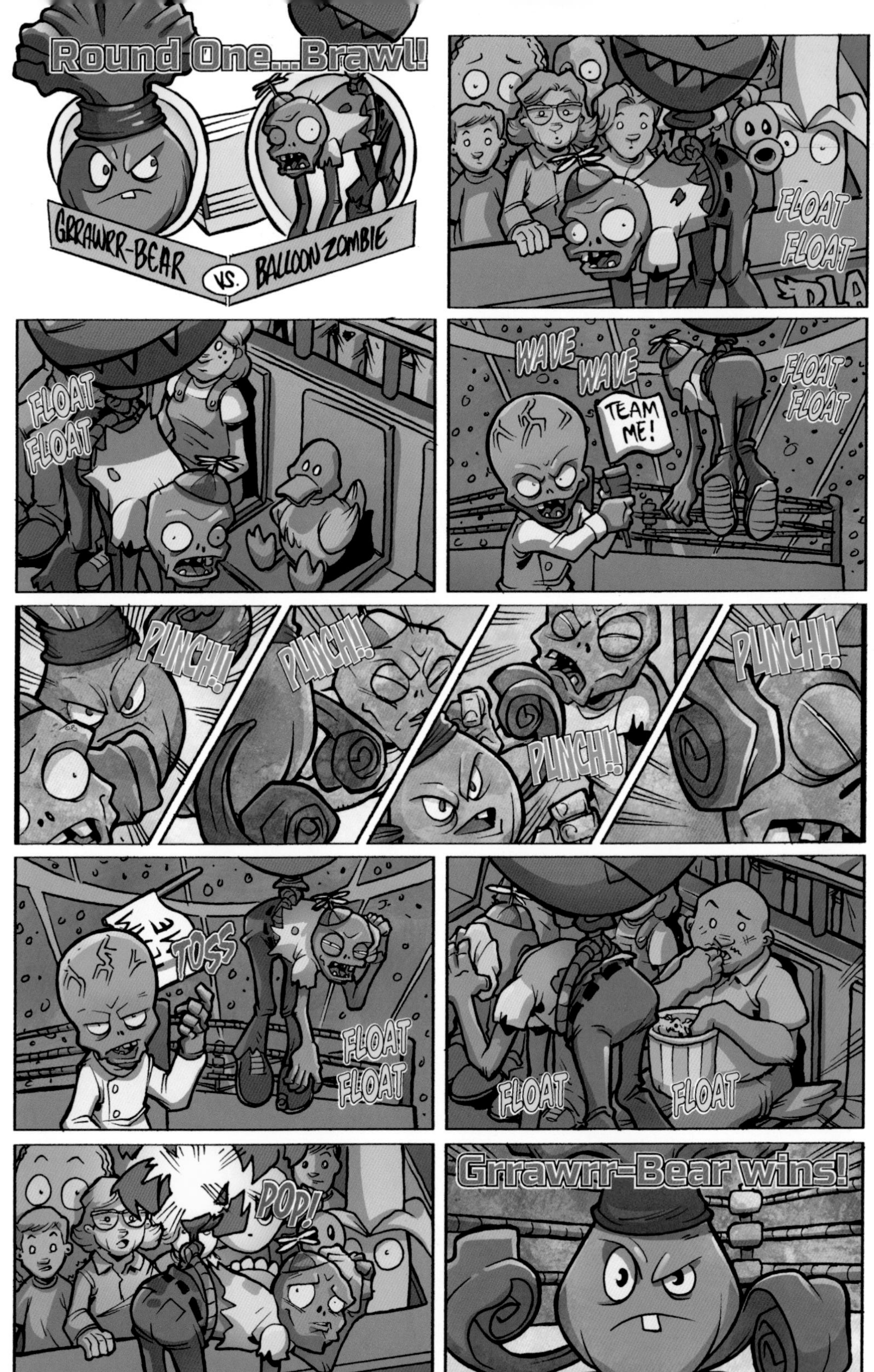
Round One...Brawl!
GRRAWRR-BEAR
VS.
BALLOON ZOMBIE
FLOAT
FLOAT
FLOAT
FLOAT
WAVE
WAVE
TEAM ME!
FLOAT
FLOAT
PUNCH!!
PUNCH!!
PUNCH!!
PUNCH!!
TOSS
FLOAT
FLOAT
FLOAT
FLOAT
POP!
Grrawrr-Bear wins!

SAD TO THINK THIS MIGHT BE THE LAST TIME WE EVER USE THE MOBILE BREAD-MAKING TRUCK.
WE DRIVE RIGHT UP TO YOUR MOUTH
"TRY OUR SIGNATURE "SWEATY BEET B-RED LOAF" OR MUNCH ON A BURGUNDY BAGUETTE!"
WITH ME SELLING THE FACTORY, WRATHBUNS BREAD WILL BE NO MORE.
I ONLY WISH WE COULD HAVE FOUND SOME SPECIAL INGREDIENT THAT WOULD HAVE MADE PEOPLE EXCITED ABOUT MY BREAD.

SOME WONDERFUL THING ADDED TO THE RECIPE THAT WOULD HAVE CHANGED EVERYTHING.

I'M SORRY, MR. TOP HAT WITH MUSTACHE. I WISH THINGS COULD BE DIFFERENT, TOO.
squeak squeak
trundle trundle

NOW, COME ON. THE TOURNAMENT HAS BEGUN.
WE SHOULD GO INSIDE AND SEE HOW THINGS TURN OUT.
IT'S USELESS TO HOPE FOR A MIRACLE.

SQUAWK! SQUAWK!

FLIP FLOP FLIBBLE!
WADDLE
WADDLE

GROMHOGG!
WADDLE
WADDLE
WADDLE

SQUAWK! SQUAWK!
SQUAWK! SQUAWK!

KREGG GREKK LOOGIE LOPPER!
FLAP
FLAP
FLAP

ROLL ROLL THUMP
THWOOP!
GRAB!

GRABBLE?
CHUGGA
CHUGGA
CHUGGA
CHONK!

CATTAIL
VS.
MR. STUBBINS
MEANWHILE...
Round One...Fight!
!
FWOOSH
Mr. Stubbins wins!

Round One... Showdown!
Potato Mine vs. Zombie Yeti!

BLINK
BLINK
SIZZLE
Potato Mine wins!

Round One...Face-Off!
SNOW PEA
VS.
BUNGEE ZOMBIE

FREEZE
Snow Pea wins!

MEANWHILE...
HMMM... THE ACCURSED PLANTS ARE WINNING TOO MANY OF THESE FIGHTS...
...AND I NEED TO WIN IN ORDER TO BUILD MY GLORIOUSLY INGLORIOUS ZOMBIE FACTORY.
HOW MUCH TO CHEAT
HARDLY AT ALL
FAIRLY OFTEN
MOST OF THE TIME
SO MUCH CHEATING!
PERHAPS I'D BEST ACCELERATE THE SPEED OF MY CHEATING?

YES! IT'S THE ONLY THING TO DO, BECAUSE CRAZY DAVE IS CERTAINLY PLANNING TO CHEAT IN HUNDREDS OF NEFARIOUS WAYS!
FAIRLY OFTEN
MOST OF THE TIME
CHNNG
SO MUCH CHEATING!

ALSO MEANWHILE...
WHAT'S CRAZY DAVE DOING? SHOULDN'T HE BE CONCENTRATING ON THE FIGHTS?
FOOF-FLAMMEL HORSEY-CORSEY!
HE SAYS HE'S DOING IMPORTANT RESEARCH WITH A NEW PLANT HE DISCOVERED. A TYPE OF GRASS.

A NEW PLANT? REALLY?! WHAT IS IT?

SWSH
SWSH
SWSH

IT'S A GRASSO.
?!

ANOTHER MEANWHILE...
CHERRY BOMB
VS.
TUGBOAT
Round One...Fight!
TUGBOAT?
Z-TECH BLAST PROOF SHIELD
Tugboat wins!
Round One...Clash!
?!?!
SCAREDY-SHROOM
ZOMBOSS
ZOMBOSS-BRAND HOT SAUCE WITH "DIRTY SOCK" FLAVORING!
Zomboss wins!
Round One... Let's Scuffle!
NIGEL
CHOMPER
VS.
BLIMPBOTTOM
Nigel Blimp-bottom wins!
SIZZLE
SIZZLE
COUGH! HACK! COUGH!

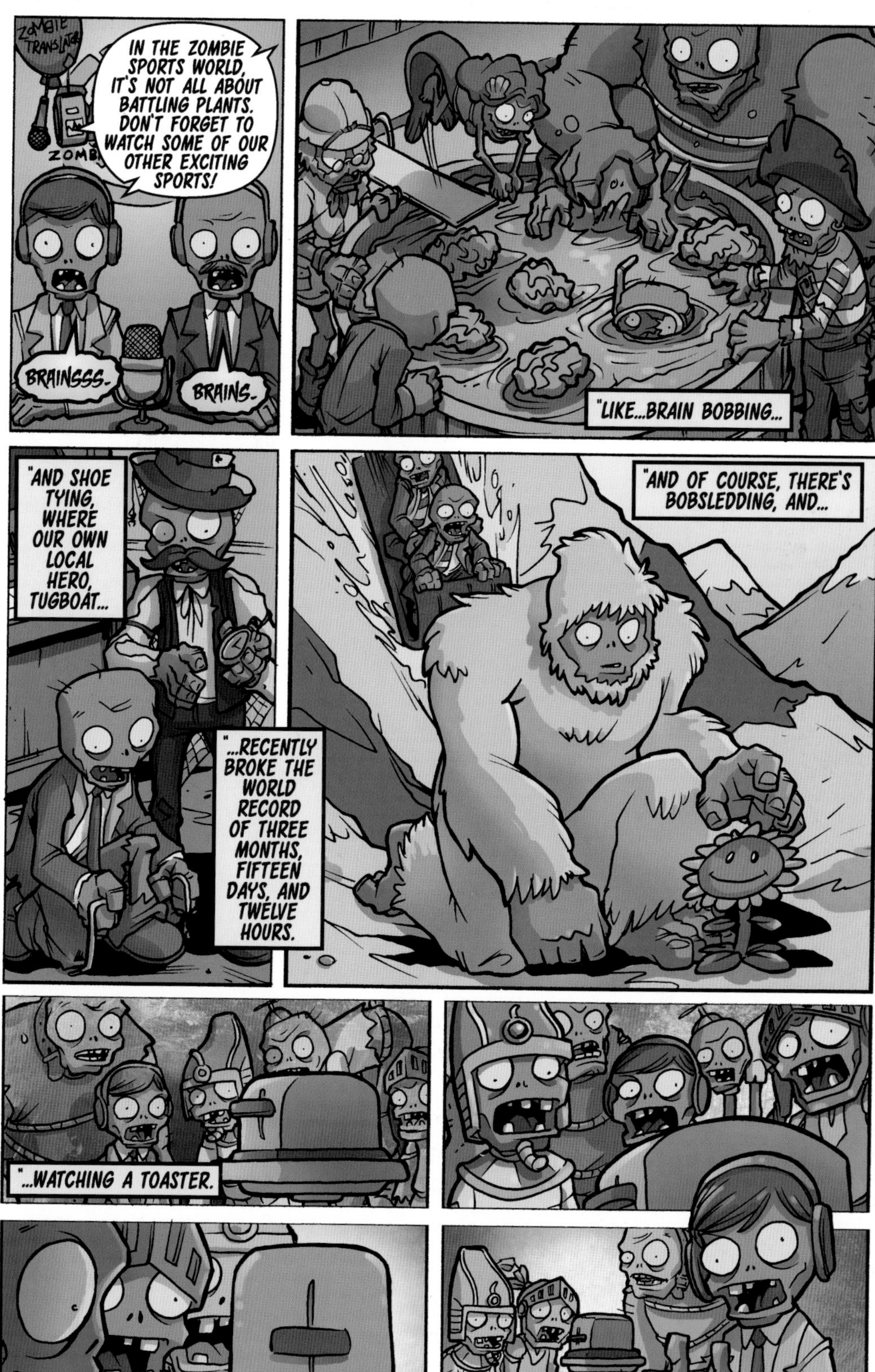
ZOMBIE TRANSLATOR
ZOMBIE
IN THE ZOMBIE SPORTS WORLD, IT'S NOT ALL ABOUT BATTLING PLANTS. DON'T FORGET TO WATCH SOME OF OUR OTHER EXCITING SPORTS!
BRAINSSS.
BRAINS.
"LIKE...BRAIN BOBBING...
"AND SHOE TYING, WHERE OUR OWN LOCAL HERO, TUGBOAT...
"...RECENTLY BROKE THE WORLD RECORD OF THREE MONTHS, FIFTEEN DAYS, AND TWELVE HOURS.
"AND OF COURSE, THERE'S BOBSLEDDING, AND...
"...WATCHING A TOASTER.
"EXCITING STUFF!"

NOW LET'S GET BACK TO THE TOURNAMENT, WITH A...
Round One Rumble!
Squash vs. Gargantuar!

THWONNK!!
Gargantuar wins!

Round One...Fight!
CRAZY DAVE
VS.
DISCO ZOMBIE
Crazy Dave wins!

Round One...Ruckus!
NATE
VS.
BUCKET HEAD
BANG
BANG
BANGITY
BANG!!!
Nate Timely wins!

ICE-CREAM BREAK!
I'D HOPED WE WOULD WIN A FEW MORE OF THESE FIRST-ROUND FIGHTS. THE ZOMBIES ARE STRONGER THAN I'D THOUGHT.

WELL, I WON *MY* FIGHT, AND *YOURS* IS COMING UP. YOU SHOULD WIN THAT.
GLAD I DON'T HAVE TO GO AGAINST THAT *GARGANTUAR* THOUGH. HE'S *HUGE!*

WE MIGHT NEED TO FIGHT HIM IN THE LATER ROUNDS, YOU KNOW.
OH, RIGHT. THIS COULD BE BAD.

GROB-FLOGGLE!
UNCLE DAVE HAS AN IDEA.

SLOOG-BROFFLE *KLARG!*
UM, HE SAYS HIS IDEA IS...

...HE COULD EAT *YOUR* ICE CREAM TOO.

THIS IS NOT HELPING.

FIGHT!
BREAK TIME IS OVER!

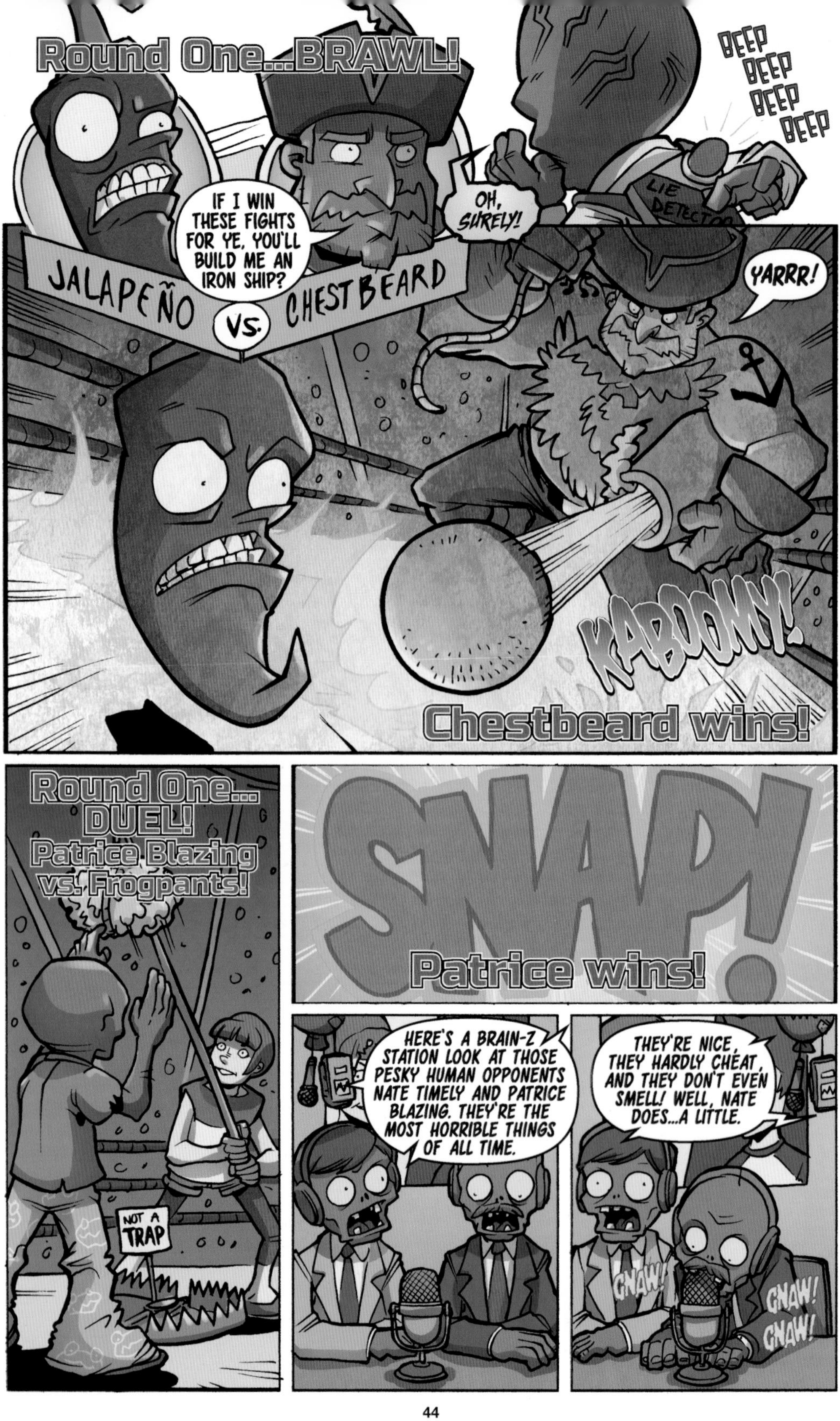

Round One...BRAWL!

IF I WIN THESE FIGHTS FOR YE, YOU'LL BUILD ME AN IRON SHIP?

OH, SURELY!

BEEP BEEP BEEP BEEP

LIE DETECTOR

JALAPEÑO VS. CHESTBEARD

YARRR!

KABOOM!

Chestbeard wins!

POP SMART BR
ICE CREAM
"BRAIN FREEZE NEVER TASTED SO GOOD!"
MEANWHILE, AT I-SCREAM, THE ZOMBIE ICE CREAM SHOPPE...
I DO NOT LIKE THE WAY THIS TOURNAMENT IS GOING. I CAN'T LOSE THAT FACTORY! IT MUST BE MINE! MINE!
SQUICK!

BECAUSE OF THAT, IT'S TIME TO INITIATE A SECRET PROJECT THAT I HAVE GIVEN THE MYSTERIOUS CODE NAME OF...

...PROJECT CHEAT A LOT UNTIL WE WIN!

HMM...LOOKS LIKE IT'S ALSO TIME TO INITIATE ANOTHER PROJECT.
THIS ONE IS CALLED...

...I'M TAKING YOUR ICE CREAM.

Round One...GENTLEMEN'S DISAGREEMENT!

MELON-PULT vs. SCREENDOOR ZOMBIE

FWOOSH

BRAINS?

Melon-pult wins!

ZOMBIE TRANSLATOR
ROUND ONE... OVER
WE'RE PRETTY EVEN NOW, WHICH IS SURPRISING CONSIDERING HOW INFERIOR PLANTS ARE, HOW WEAK HUMANS ARE, AND HOW NEITHER WILL EVEN CHEAT, WHICH SHOWS A COMPLETE LACK OF EVIL ON THEIR PARTS!

ZOMBIE TRANSLATOR
AND NOW A COMMERCIAL BREAK

HI! I'M ZOMBOSS, YOUR LEADER. I'M HERE TO TALK ABOUT POP SMARTS, THE DELICIOUS BRAIN-FLAVORED TREAT!
POP SMARTS
POP SMARTS
YOU SHOULD BUY POP SMARTS. UNLESS I WANT THEM. THEN YOU SHOULD NOT.
BECAUSE THEN I WILL DESTROY YOU.
POP SMARTS

ZOMBIE TRANSLATOR
OKAY! THAT WAS...NICE. WHAT A GREAT GUY THAT ZOMBOSS IS! UNLESS HE'S DESTROYING YOU. AND NOW, LET'S TAKE A LOOK AT THE VIGOROUS TRAINING REGIMENS OF SOME OF OUR ATHLETES!

PUNCH
PUNCH
PUNCH

RAMP!
RING OF FUR

PIZZA

PUNCH
PUNCH
PUNCH

BRAINS
STILL TASTY

KICK
KICK
KICK

TURN THAT CAMERA OFF!

P-TOO
P-TOO

ELSEWHERE...
TIME TO RELEASE MY BEAUTIFUL BADGUETTE...A DEVICE DISGUISED AS A BAGUETTE IN ORDER TO BLEND IN PERFECTLY WITH THE BREAD THEY'RE SERVING, BUT...
PLANTS ZOMBIES
LUCHA LIBRE WRESTLING TOURNAMENT
...IT'S ACTUALLY A WONDERFUL MECHANISM TO TRIGGER A TREMENDOUS BURST OF DARKNESS THAT WILL STEAL ALL SUN POWER FROM THE PLANTS, RENDERING THEM HELPLESS!
HA HA HA HA!

MY PLAN IS FLAWLESS.
HA HA HA HA!

HMM...I DON'T REMEMBER THIS HALLWAY.
GURKK!

WHO'S THIS?

MUST BE THE NEW GUY.
WOW, WHAT AN UGLY MASK. OH, WELL, LET'S...

...GET HIM IN THE RING.
TOSS!

GAH!
SUPLEX!

FWOO!
GRAAH!
DOUBLE FLYING SUPLEX!

UAAH!!
FLAMING SKY DRAGON SUPLEX!
FWOOOSH!

KRAKKA-KOOOOM!
ULTIMATE POWER ATOMIC DESTRUCTION MIND-BLOWING BUTT-CLENCHING SUPLEX!!
GAAHH!!

WOW! SOUNDS LIKE THINGS ARE REALLY SHAKING NEXT DOOR.
KRAKKA-BRAKKA-BOOOOM!
SOME SORT OF LUCHA LIBRE WRESTLING CHAMPIONSHIP, I THINK.
WISH WE COULD WATCH, BUT OUR NEXT ROUND IS ABOUT TO START.
JUNKY MCJUNK'S JUNK FOOD!
HOPEFULLY THIS LINE WILL GO FASTER. THE BREAD SEEMS REALLY POPULAR ALL OF A SUDDEN, AND I'M HUNGRY AND--
WOO! I GOT US SOME FOOD! CANDY-TOP PIZZA AND PIZZA-TOP CANDY!
UMM...OKAY. I WANTED TO TRY SOME OF THAT BREAD, THOUGH. PEOPLE SURE SEEM TO LIKE IT. IT'S IMPORTANT TO EAT RIGHT AND--
MMM! THEY HAD PIZZA MILKSHAKES TOO!
THAT ALL LOOKS...UH... DELICIOUS, NATE. BUT THERE'S NO WAY YOU CAN EAT THAT ALL BEFORE THE NEXT ROUND...
...BEGINS.
DONE! LET'S GO!

MEANWHILE...

OKAY, MY LAST PLAN HAD SOME... PROBLEMS. BUT THIS TIME IT WILL WORK!

YOU MINERS TAKE THIS BADGUETTE...

TAPE

STAPLES

GLUE

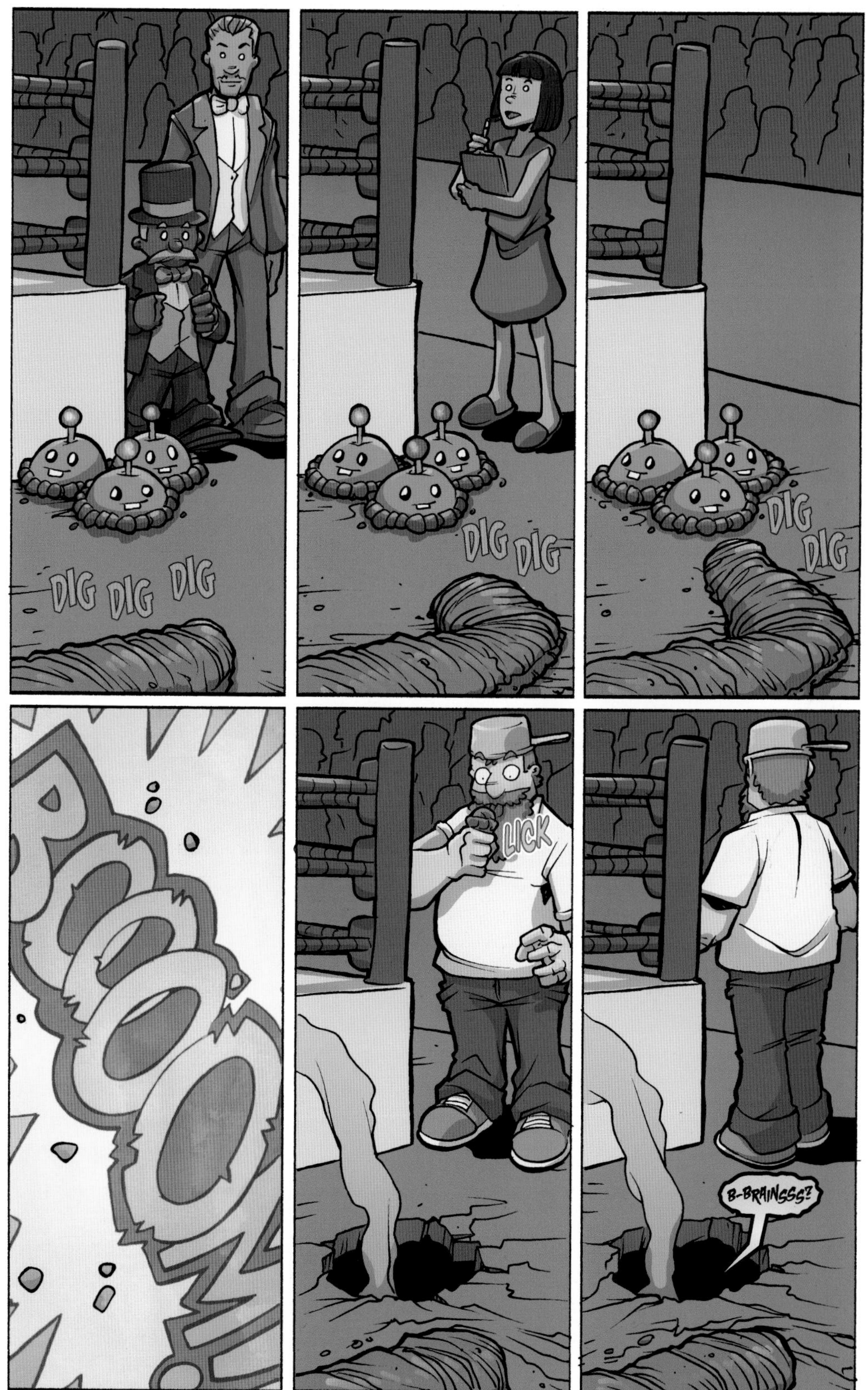
DIG DIG DIG
DIG DIG
DIG DIG
LICK
B-BRAINSSS?

ZOMBIE TRANSLATOR
AND NOW, OUR SECOND ROUND, AS THE WINNERS FROM THE FIRST ROUND MOVE ON TO NEW OPPONENTS!
ZOMBIE SPORTS NETWORK
SECOND ROUND!

ZOMBIE TRANSLATOR
THERE ARE SOME INTERESTING MATCHUPS AHEAD. SHOULD BE AN EXCITING BATTLE TO THE FINISH, BEFORE THE PLANTS ARE ULTIMATELY FINISHED OFF!

"NOW, A MESSAGE FROM OUR SPONSOR, ZOM-B UNIVERSITY, HOME OF THE WORLD CHAMPION FLAMING LACES SHOE-TYING TEAM, WITH A WORD FROM PROFESSOR THADDEUS T. BRAINPOWER."

BRAINS?

GNAW!
GNAW!
GNAW!

LET THE FIGHTS...BEGIN AGAIN!
HYPNO-SHROOM
VS.
MR. STUBBINS
Second Round... Fight!

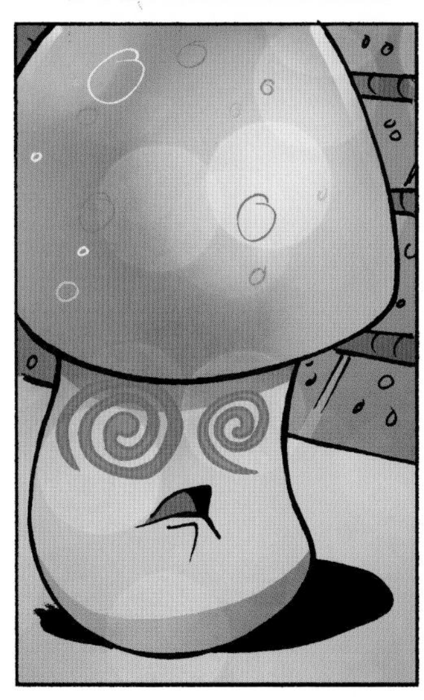

GLINT
GLEAM
GLINT
BRRRUMMM

GLINT
GLEAM
GLINT
??

REFLECT!
!!

Mr. Stubbins wins!

Second Round... FACE-OFF!

SNOW PEA VS. GARGANTUAR

Gargantuar wins!

Second Round... SHOWDOWN!

NATE VS. TUGBOAT

Nate Timely wins!

TUGBOAT?

MR. TOP HAT WITH MUSTACHE! OVER HERE! I WANTED YOU TO SEE THIS!
5

LOOK AT THESE LINES! THE BREAD TRUCK IS WORKING FURIOUSLY IN ORDER TO MEET THIS DEMAND!
OOO! HOW DID MY BREAD BECOME *THIS* POPULAR?!

I WONDERED THAT TOO, SO I HAD OUR BREAD TECHNICIANS TEST THIS LATEST BATCH OF BREAD AND...IT TURNS OUT THERE ARE FOREIGN INGREDIENTS!
HM.
THERE'S ICE CREAM.
HM.
AND THE BREATH OF, I BELIEVE, A FROG.
HM.

SO BE IT! LET'S *ADD* THESE NEW INGREDIENTS TO THE *OFFICIAL* RECIPE!
GO TO THE ICE-CREAM FACTORIES AND GET ME A MILLION GALLONS!
GO TO THE SWAMPS AND HIRE A THOUSAND FROGS!
scribble scribble

HOW DID THOSE NEW INGREDIENTS GET INTO MY BREAD?
WE HAVE NO IDEA. PERHAPS IT'S THE *MIRACLE* WE WERE HOPING FOR.

WE'LL PROBABLY NEVER KNOW.
SLLURP
SLLURP

Second Round... FIGHT!
PATRICE
VS.
IMP
??
HUG ME
HUG ME
PUNNNT!
Patrice wins!
Second Round... RUMBLE!
YARRRRR !!!
Grrawrr-Bear vs. Chestbeard!
EEEAARRR!!!
WHOOOSH
OOP. A BEARD T-TRIMMER?
Grrawrr-Bear wins!

AND THEN...
UNSUSPICIOUS CUSTODIAN
THIS TIME, MY PLAN IS FLAWLESS. MY AMAZING CUSTODIAL DISGUISE WILL ALLOW ME TO...

...SNEAK BENEATH THE RING WITH NO ONE NOTICING.

HMM... DARKER IN HERE THAN I THOUGHT IT WOULD BE.
UNSUSPICIOUS CUSTODI

CAN'T SEE ANYTHING. NOT SURE WHERE TO PUT THIS BADGUETTE.

LUCKILY, I ALWAYS CARRY MY Z-TECH FLASHLIGHT, SO THAT I CAN CLEARLY SEE...

BLINK
BLINK
BLINK

...ALL OF THESE EXPLOSIVE MUSHROOMS.

Second Round... FIGHT!
MELON-PULT VS. ZOMBOSS
?
??
??
KABOOOOOOOM!
??
??
Zomboss wins!
WHAMMMP!

Second Round... DUEL!
POTATO MINE
VS.
NIGEL BLIMPBOTTOM
GNAW!
GNAW!
GNAW!

Z-TECH
BOMBPROOF SHELTER
PUNISHMENT CHAMBER
BEDROOM
SLEEPS 25
BOOM!

GNAW!
GNAW!
GNAW!
Nigel Blimpbottom wins!

BOO!
BOO!
GRR!
GOOD BREAD!
JERK ZOMBIES!

Round Two... LAST FIGHT!
NEWSPAPER ZOMBIE DOOMED?
PEASHOOTER
VS.
NEWSPAPER ZOMBIE

WSPAPER ZOMBIE
DOOMED!
Peashooter wins!

MEANWHILE, NOT FAR AWAY...
I'VE GOT AN ALMOST COMPLETE SET OF THE PLANTS VS. ZOMBIES: BATTLE EXTRAVAGONZO TRADING CARDS!
ME TOO!

I'VE GOT THE PEASHOOTER CARD AND MELON-PULT AND-- I HOPE I'M PRONOUNCING THIS RIGHT--GRRAWRR-BEAR THE ULTIMATE FACE PUNCHER!

AND I'VE GOT DISCO ZOMBIE, GARGANTUAR, AND POTATO MINE!

LOOK, I'VE GOT AN AUTOGRAPHED CARD FROM NATE TIMELY!
YOU CAN TELL IT'S AUTHENTIC BECAUSE YOU CAN SEE ALL THE PIZZA STAINS!

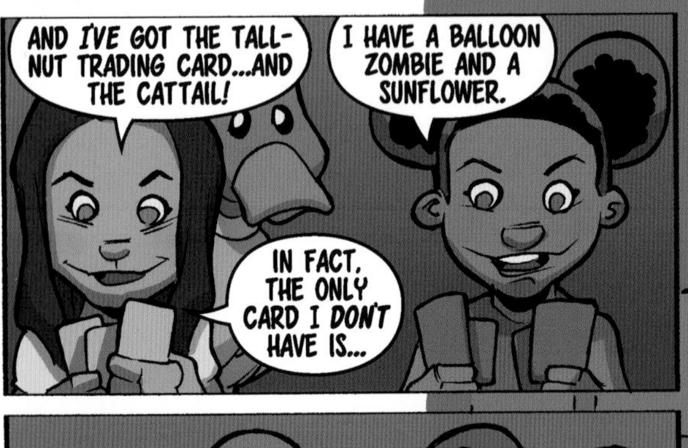
AND I'VE GOT THE TALL-NUT TRADING CARD...AND THE CATTAIL!
I HAVE A BALLOON ZOMBIE AND A SUNFLOWER.
IN FACT, THE ONLY CARD I DON'T HAVE IS...

...THE ZOMBOSS CARD, BECAUSE...

"...HE BOUGHT THEM ALL."
MINE. ALL MINE!

MORE MEANWHILE...
ZOMBIE STRATEGY ROOM NO HUMANS (EXCEPT BRAIN DONORS)
NATE, I'LL DISTRACT THESE ZOMBIES WHILE YOU SNEAK IN AND GET A PEEK AT THE ZOMBIES' CHEAT PLAN, OKAY?

I'M ON IT!
JUST BE QUIET, OKAY?
NO PROBLEM! NOBODY WILL EVER NOTICE I'M THERE!
OKAY...GET READY. I'LL DISTRACT THE GUARDS.

HEY, YOU GUYS! LOOK! A BALLOON!

BRAINSSS...

ZOMBIE STRATEGY ROOM NO HUMANS!

THE CHEAT PLAN! I FOUND IT!

OOPS.
WUNNK!

CRUMBLE
OOPS!

SQUAWK!
UGH! NOW I STEPPED ON A DUCK?
WHY'S THERE A DUCK HERE?

PUNCH PUNCH
SWAT!
DUCK PUNCH
DANG! I'M SORRY!

WOOP!
SKRASHH!
PUNCH PUNCH
SWAT!
DUCK PUNCH
AGAIN?

AND NOW IT'S TIME FOR ROUND THREE! OUR OWN GARGANTUAR WILL BE GOING TWICE IN THIS ROUND, TO MAKE UP FOR THERE BEING MORE REMAINING PLANTS THAN ZOMBIES. SO WE'LL HAVE TWICE THE GARGANTUAR FUN!

IT'S ALL GETTING SO EXCITING, I CAN HARDLY THINK! I, IN FACT, CANNOT THINK AT ALL. THINKING IS JUST NOT MY THING. OKAY! ROUND THREE!

MMM!

THIS BREAD IS SO GOOD!

YAAAY!

BRAINS.

Round Three...FIGHT!

PEASHOOTER VS. ZOMBOSS

P-TOO

P-TOO

P-TOO

MUNCH

MUNCH

MUNCH

Z-TECH

Z-TECH BRAND RUBBER BAND.

LIQUORICE-BRAIN POP SMARTS.

Round Three...

SHOWDOWN!

CRAZY DAVE VS. MR. STUBBINS

Ice cream eating contest!

Mr. Stubbins wins!

PATRICE VS. NIGEL BLIMPBOTTOM

Round Three... FACE OFF!

HEY, REFEREE! THAT'S *NOT* NIGEL! THAT'S JUST THE *GARGANTUAR* IN A *NIGEL* MASK! THE ZOMBIES ARE *CHEATING!*

OBJECTION... DENIED!

Round Three...FIGHT!

NATE TIMELY VS. GARGANTUAR

WHAT? NO!! NOT YET! *MY PIZZAAA!!*

THOOM!

SPLUTTCH!
HOW'S THAT SUNSHINE
SUNSHINE PIZZA
SUNSHINE PIZZA
UH-OH!
TMMP
TMMP
!!
FWOOSH
!!
PLUMMET
KTHONK
SLIP!
Nate Timely wins!
NATE! YOU WON!
BUT... MY PIZZA! MY EVERYTHING PIZZA MEANT EVERYTHING TO ME!

AND SO, SOON...
OKAY, NATE. WE'RE WAY BEHIND THE ZOMBIES NOW.
YOU'RE THE ONLY ONE OF US WHO ADVANCED TO THE FOURTH ROUND.
THAT MEANS YOU HAVE TO WIN ALL YOUR FIGHTS IN ORDER FOR US TO WIN THE TOURNAMENT.
YOU'LL HAVE TO BEAT THE GARGANTUAR AGAIN--TWICE!

AND YOU'LL HAVE TO BEAT MR. STUBBINS.
AND... YOU'LL HAVE TO BEAT ZOMBOSS.

NOW, MY UNCLE DAVE WANTS TO GIVE YOU SOME LAST-MINUTE ADVICE.
GROK TODDLE CHIM FLIBBET! CHOPPLE PLATYPUS BORKFLAIN!

HARPLE GLORN! FOZZLE-POP!
HE SAYS TO WATCH OUT FOR THE GARGANTUAR'S CLUB. AND TO BEWARE OF MR. STUBBINS'S QUILLS.

QUARRG! PLORG-RANG CHUDDER DING!
AND TO...UH, RUB ICE CREAM ALL OVER YOUR ARMS, BECAUSE IT'S GOOD FOR YOUR SKIN.
ALSO, HE LOVES EATING MOTORIZED TOAST.

SOGGY GLORK! WEGGLE TEGGLE PEGGLE!!
HE SAYS THAT HIS EARS ARE UPSIDE DOWN, GOLF BALLS AREN'T A GOOD BREAKFAST FOOD...
...DISCO COULD'VE SAVED THE DINOSAURS...

...HE ADVISES YOU TO CARRY EXTRA NOSTRILS, AND--
YEAH... I THINK WE'RE DONE HERE.

AND SO...
NATE TIMELY
VS.
MR. STUBBINS
Round Four... RUMBLE!
SCURRY!
SCURRY!
SCURRY!
SCURRY!
CHUBBY CHOMP!
A LOT OF GUM!
SCURRY!
SCURRY!
SCURRY!
SCURRY!
CHEW
CHEW
CHEW
CHEW
CHEW
SCURRY!
SCURRY!
SCURRY!
SCURRY!
PTOO!
GLORRK!
Nate Timely wins!

CAN'T DISAPPOINT THE FANS!

HERE'S AN AUTOGRAPH FOR YOU. AND YOU. AND YOU. AND YOU. AND YOU.

DISGUISED PLANTS!

AND YOU. AND YOU. AND YOU.

NATE TIMELY VS. GARGANTUAR
THOOM!
THOOM!
THOOM!
Round Four... BIG SCARY SCUFFLE!

FWOOSH
DODGE!

HRFF! HRFF! PHEW!
SURRENDER
Forfeit! Nate Timely wins!

HE WASN'T EVEN TRYING.
PLOP PLIPPLE!
UNCLE DAVE SAYS THAT THE GARGANTUAR KNOWS YOU'LL HAVE TO FIGHT HIM AGAIN, SO HE WAS JUST WEARING YOU OUT...THIS TIME.
AND...UH... DAVE ALSO SAYS THAT PICKLES LOOK WEIRD IN SHORTS.

PICKLES IN SHORTS? YEAH, I SUPPOSE THAT'S TRUE.

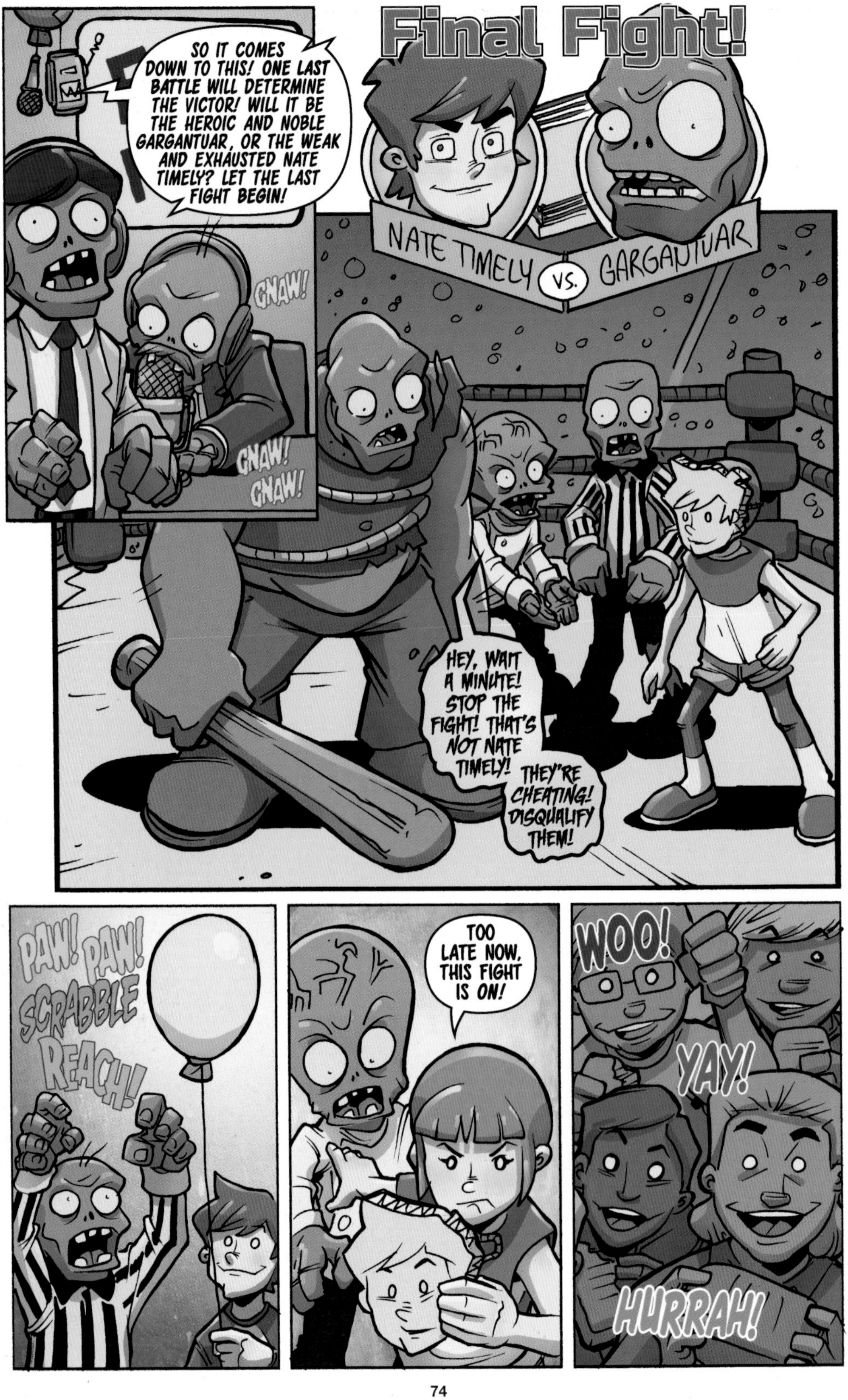

Final Fight!

SO IT COMES DOWN TO THIS! ONE LAST BATTLE WILL DETERMINE THE VICTOR! WILL IT BE THE HEROIC AND NOBLE GARGANTUAR, OR THE WEAK AND EXHAUSTED NATE TIMELY? LET THE LAST FIGHT BEGIN!

GNAW!

GNAW! GNAW!

NATE TIMELY VS. GARGANTUAR

HEY, WAIT A MINUTE! STOP THE FIGHT! THAT'S NOT NATE TIMELY!

THEY'RE CHEATING! DISQUALIFY THEM!

YANK!
GRASSO!
??
??
DUCK DISTRACTION!!
FWOO!
FROG'S BREATH ICE CREAM!!!
GUHHHHH...
Plants win!
Plants win!
PLANTS HAVE DEFEATED THE ZOMBIES!
TOPPLE!

IT IS WITH GREAT PLEASURE THAT I ANNOUNCE YOU AS THE *WINNERS* OF THE PLANTS VERSUS ZOMBIES *BATTLE EXTRAVAGONZO!*
CAN CRAZY DAVE BUY THE FACTORY NOW?
WELL...UH...NO. I MEAN, *LOOK* AT THIS AUDIENCE.
Beet Bread
YOU SEE, DURING THIS TOURNAMENT WE'VE SOLD *SO* MANY OF OUR SWEATY BEET B-RED LOAVES AND BURGUNDY BAGUETTES, AND GOTTEN SO MUCH GREAT ADVERTISING, THAT...
LICK LICK
SLRP
...THE FACTORY IS NO LONGER FOR SALE.
BLEMPPLE PLORK FRIBBLE-PLONG!
FIVE!
FIVE!
FIVE!
FIVE!
DAVE SAYS THAT'S *GREAT!* HE REALLY DIDN'T WANT TO HAVE TO RUN A FACTORY, ANYWAY, AND NOW THERE'S *NO* CHANCE OF ZOMBOSS EVER GETTING IT!
TOTAL VICTORY! HIGH FIVES FOR *EVERYONE!*
HEY, LOOK!
WRATHBUNS BREAD IS MAKING *PIZZA* NOW!
WRATHBUN
PIZZA
MUNCH
MUNCH
MUNCH
WHAT?
THE END

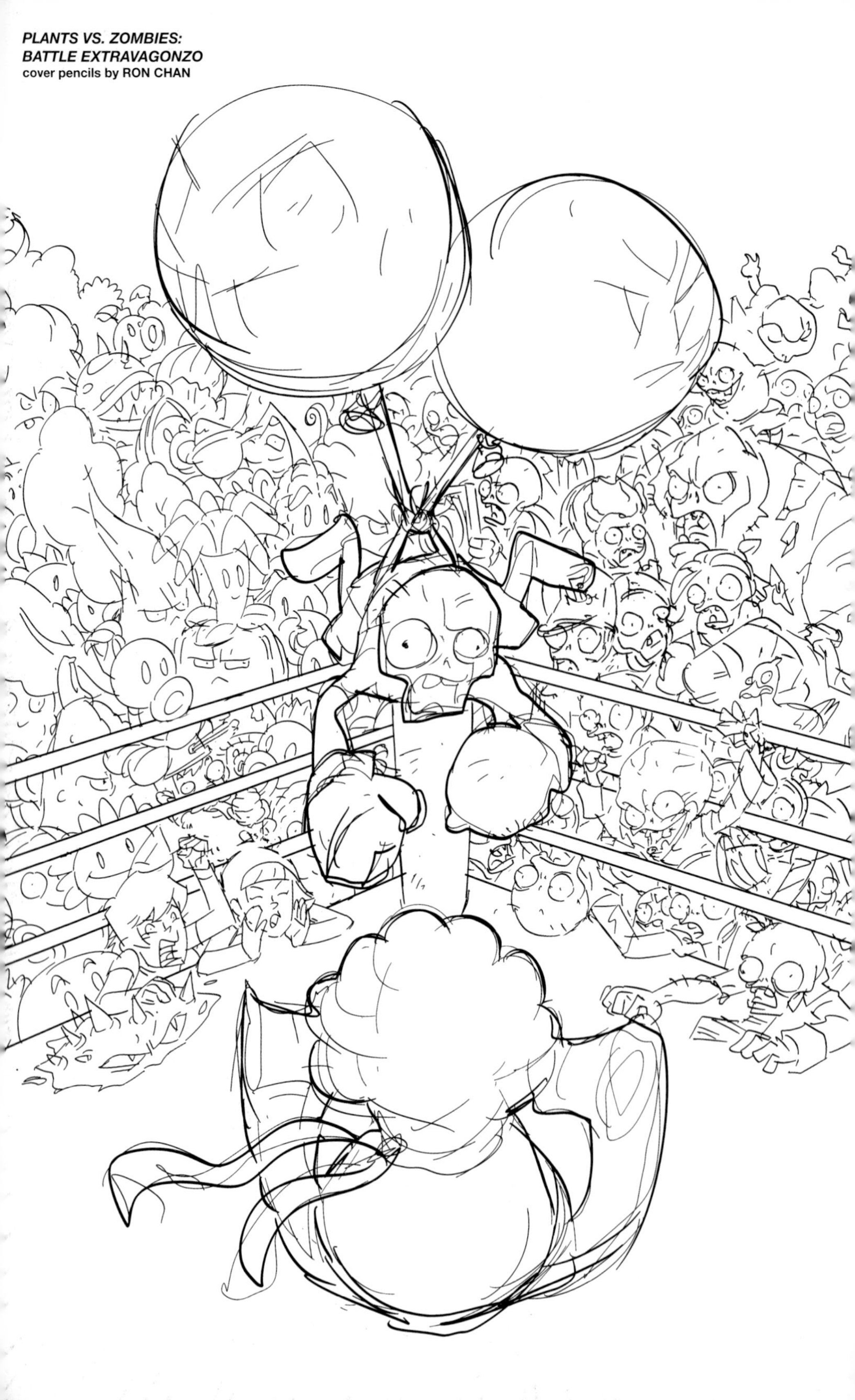

PLANTS VS. ZOMBIES:
BATTLE EXTRAVAGONZO
cover pencils by RON CHAN

PLANTS VS. ZOMBIES: BATTLE EXTRAVAGONZO
cover inks by RON CHAN

PENCIL ART FROM *BATTLE EXTRAVAGONZO* STORY PAGES 6–9 BY ARTIST TIM LATTIE!

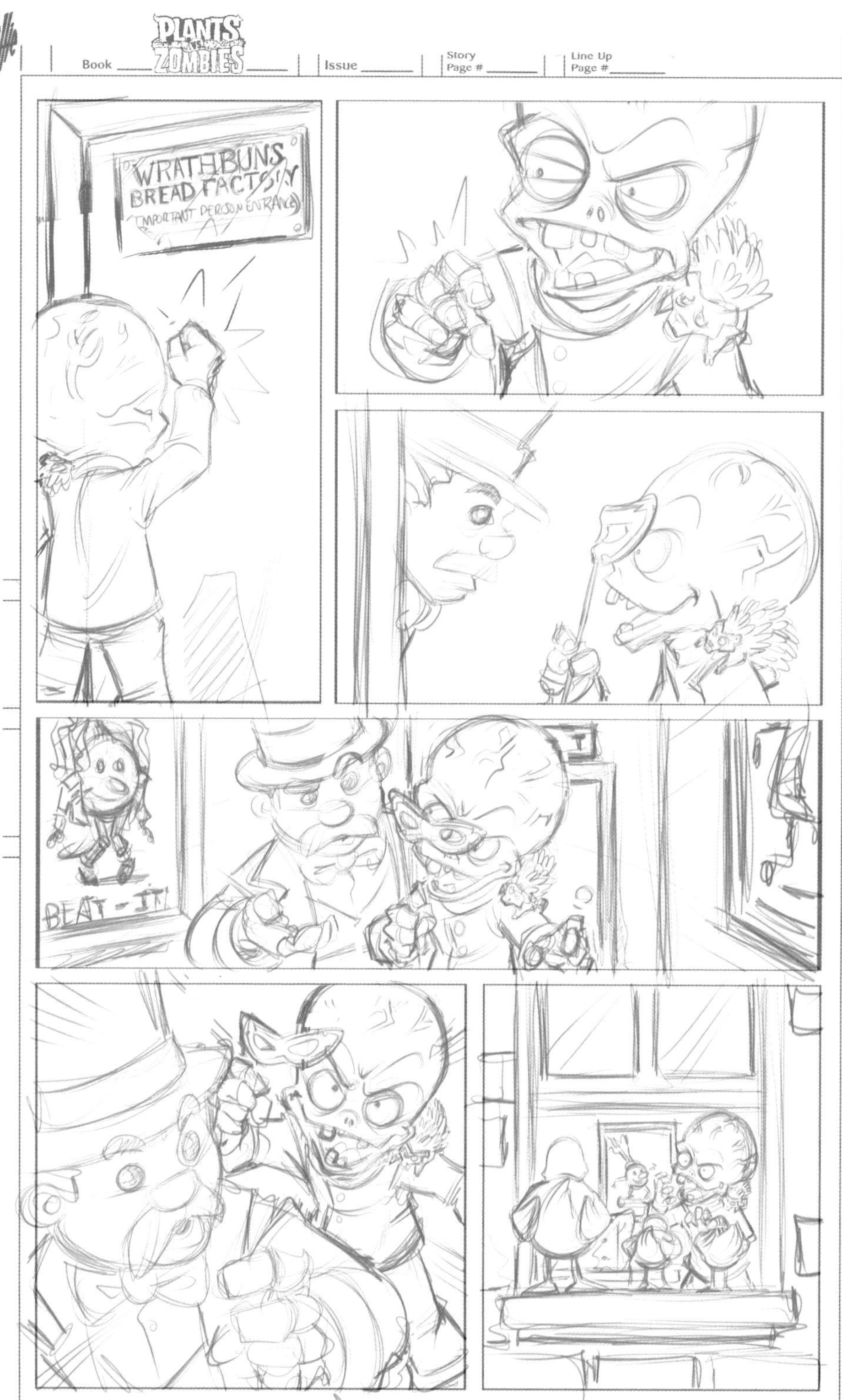
PLANTS vs ZOMBIES
Book
Issue
Story Page #
Line Up Page #
WRATHBUNS BREAD FACTORY
IMPORTANT PERSON ENTRANCE
BEAT - IT

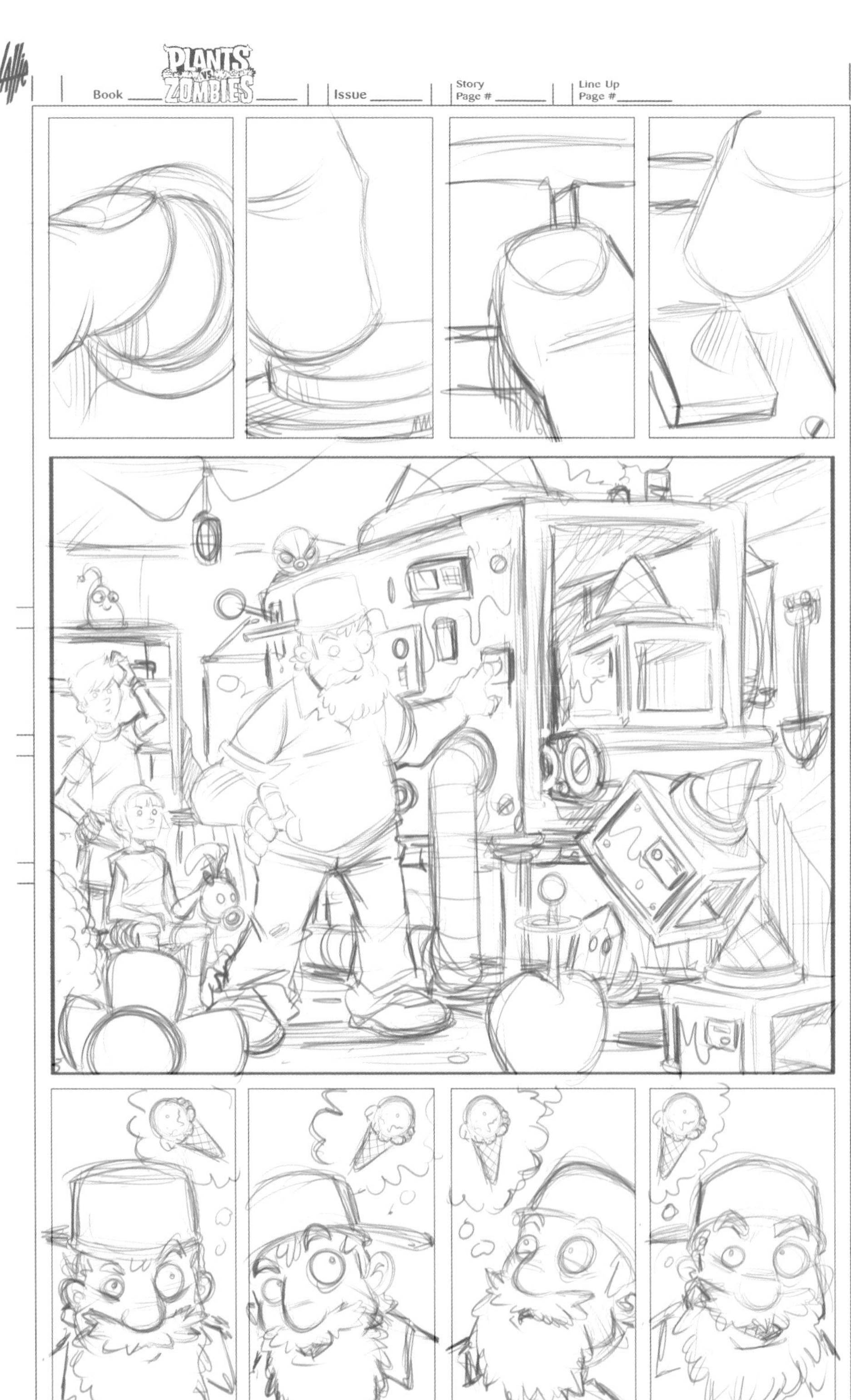
PLANTS VS ZOMBIES
Book
Issue
Story Page #
Line Up Page #

Book PLANTS vs. ZOMBIES Issue Story Page # Line Up Page #

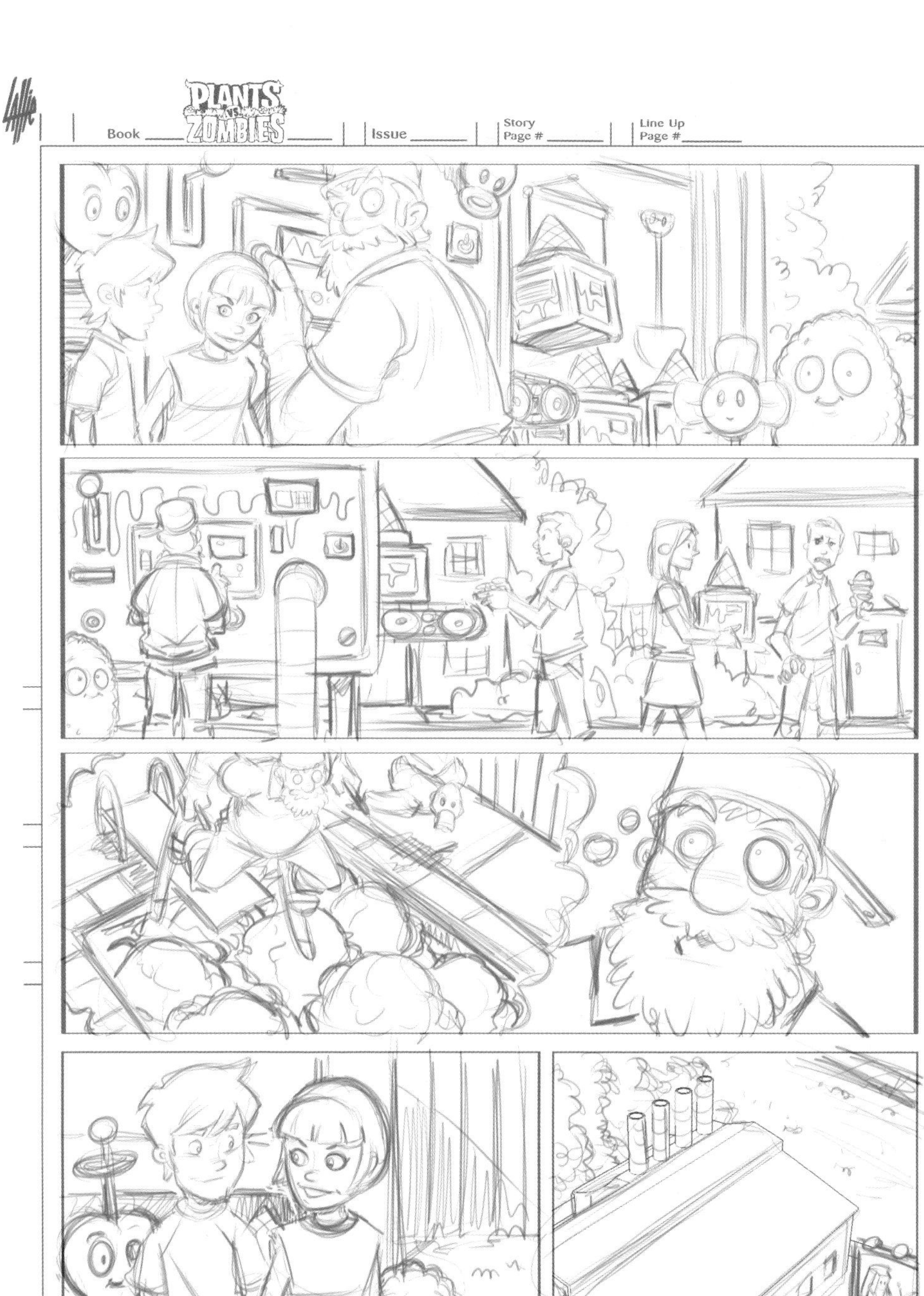

CREATOR BIOS

Paul Tobin

Tim Lattie

PAUL TOBIN enjoys that his author photo makes him look insane, and he once accidentally cut his ear with a potato chip. He doesn't know how it happened, either. Life is so full of mystery. If you ask him about the Potato Chip Incident, he'll just make up a story. That's what he does. He's written hundreds of stories for Marvel, DC, Dark Horse, and many others, including such creator-owned titles as *Colder* and *Bandette*, as well as *Prepare to Die!*—his debut novel. His *Genius Factor* series of novels about a fifth-grade genius and his war against the Red Death Tea Society debuted in March 2016 with *How to Capture an Invisible Cat*, from Bloomsbury Publishing, and continued in early 2017 with *How to Outsmart a Billion Robot Bees*. Paul has won some Very Important Awards for his writing but so far none for his karaoke skills.

TIM LATTIE, half artist, half amazing, was born and raised in Metairie, Louisiana. As a child he had a strong affinity for comic books and animation. This obsession led to him creating his own characters and stories. Later, he studied at NOCCA (New Orleans Center for Creative Arts) and SCAD (Savannah College of Art and Design). He now does graphic novels for IDW, Dark Horse, and UNICEF, as well as working on his creator-owned book about teenagers, time travel, and UFOs, called *Night Stars*! You can follow his work by going to LattieInk.com. Through the process of drawing this book, Tim has also discovered his true calling and has begun illustrating anti-plant propaganda for Zomboss's zombie army. Soon, not only Crazy Dave and his plants but all of Neighborville shall kneel before ZOMBOSS!

Matt J. Rainwater

Steve Dutro

Residing in the cool, damp forests of Portland, Oregon, **MATT J. RAINWATER** is a freelance illustrator whose work has been featured in advertising, web design, and independent video games. On top of this, he also self-publishes several comic books, including *Trailer Park Warlock*, *Garage Raja*, and *The Feeling Is Multiplied*—all of which can be found at MattJRainwater.com. His favorite zombie-bashing strategy utilizes a line of Bonk Choys with a Wall-nut front guard and Threepeater covering fire.

STEVE DUTRO is an Eisner Award-nominated comic-book letterer from Redding, California, who can also drive a tractor. He graduated from the Kubert School and has been lettering comics since the days when foil-embossed covers were cool, working for Dark Horse (*The Fifth Beatle*, *I Am a Hero*, *Planet of the Apes*, *Star Wars*), Viz, Marvel, and DC. He has submitted a request to the Department of Homeland Security that in the event of a zombie apocalypse he be put in charge of all digital freeway signs so citizens can be alerted to avoid nearby brain-eatings and the like. He finds the *Plants vs. Zombies* game to be a real stress-fest, but highly recommends the *Plants vs. Zombies* table on *Pinball FX2* for game-room hipsters.

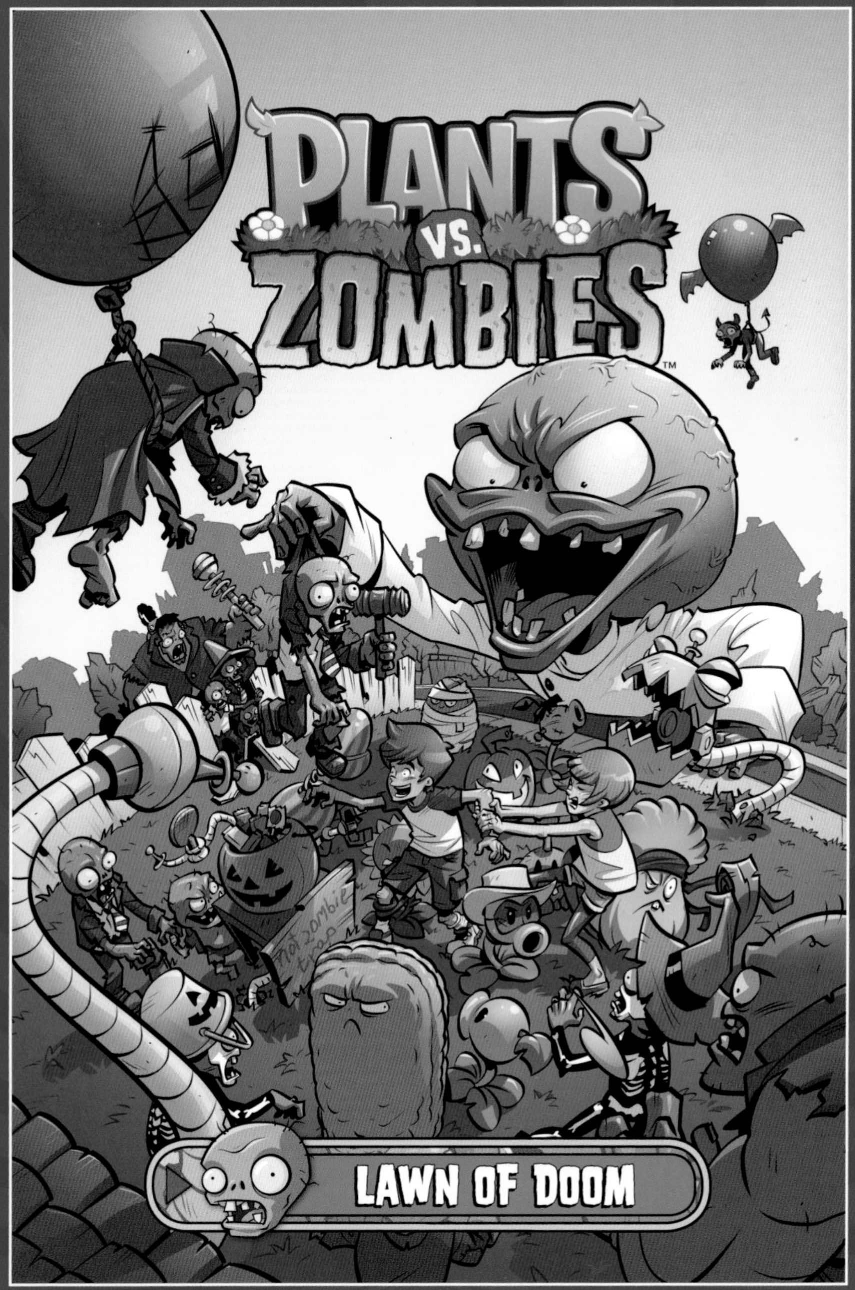

PLANTS VS. ZOMBIES: LAWN OF DOOM—MATERIALIZING OCTOBER 2017!

Halloween in Neighborville is weird enough, but now Zomboss and his zombie army want to turn the holiday into their own menacing Lawn of Doom celebration! With Zomboss filling everyone's yards with traps and special zombies, Crazy Dave, Patrice, Nate, and a batch of brave, boisterous plants fight back in contests of best tricks, best treats, and best costumes!